Cat Dissection Guide

Department of Human Science

Human Biology

Georgetown University

| PEARSON COLLECTIONS |

PEARSON

Attention bookstores: For permission to return any unsold stock, contact us at pe-uscustomreturns@pearson.com

Pearson Learning Solutions, 501 Boylston Street, Suite 900, Boston, MA 02116

A Pearson Education Company
www.pearsoned.com

ISBN 10: 1323867643

ISBN 13: 9781323867648

Printed in the USA   7 2023

Table of Contents

Getting Started—What to Expect, The Scientific Method, and Metrics

Two hundred years ago, science was largely a plaything of wealthy patrons, but today's world is dominated by science and its technology. Whether or not we believe that such domination is desirable, we all have a responsibility to try to understand the goals and methods of science that have seeded this knowledge and technological explosion.

The biosciences are very special and exciting because they open the doors to an understanding of all the wondrous workings of living things. A course in human anatomy and physiology (a subdivision of bioscience) provides such insights in relation to your own body. Although some experience in scientific studies is helpful when beginning a study of anatomy and physiology, perhaps the single most important prerequisite is curiosity.

Gaining an understanding of science is a little like becoming acquainted with another person. Even though a written description can provide a good deal of information about the person, you can never really know another unless there is personal contact. And so it is with science—if you are to know it well, you must deal with it intimately.

The laboratory is the setting for "intimate contact" with science. It is where scientists test their ideas (do research), the essential purpose of which is to provide a basis from which predictions about scientific phenomena can be made. Likewise, it will be the site of your "intimate contact" with the subject of human anatomy and physiology as you are introduced to the methods and instruments used in biological research.

For many students, human anatomy and physiology is an introductory-level course; and their scientific background exists, at best, as a dim memory. If this is your predicament, this prologue may be just what you need to fill in a few gaps and to get you started on the right track before your actual laboratory experiences begin. So—let's get to it!

The Scientific Method

Science would quickly stagnate if new knowledge were not continually derived from and added to it. The approach commonly used by scientists when they investigate various aspects of their respective disciplines is called the **scientific method.** This method is *not* a single rigorous technique that must be followed in a lockstep manner. It is nothing more or less than a logical, practical, and reliable way of approaching and solving problems of every kind—scientific or otherwise—to gain knowledge. It includes five major steps.

Step 1: Observation of Phenomena

The crucial first step involves observation of some phenomenon of interest. In other words, before a scientist can investigate anything, he or she must decide on a *problem* or focus for the investigation. In most college laboratory experiments, the problem or focus has been decided for you. However, to illustrate this important step, we will assume that you want to investigate the true nature of apples, particularly green apples. In such a case you would begin your studies by making a number of different observations concerning apples.

Step 2: Statement of the Hypothesis

Once you have decided on a focus of concern, the next step is to design a significant question to be answered. Such a question is usually posed in the form of a **hypothesis,** an unproven conclusion that attempts to explain some phenomenon. (At its crudest level, a hypothesis can be considered to be a "guess" or an intuitive hunch that tentatively explains some observation.) Generally, scientists do not restrict themselves to a single hypothesis; instead, they usually pose several and then test each one systematically.

We will assume that to accomplish step 1, you go to the supermarket and randomly select apples from several bins. When you later eat the apples, you find that the green apples are sour but that the red and yellow apples are sweet. From this observation, you might conclude *(hypothesize)* that "green apples are sour." This statement would represent your current understanding of green apples. You might also reasonably predict that if you were to buy more apples, any green ones you buy will be sour. Thus, you would have gone beyond your initial observation that "these" green apples are sour to the prediction that "all" green apples are sour.

Any good hypothesis must meet several criteria. First, *it must be testable.* This characteristic is far more important than its being correct. The test data may or may not support the hypothesis, or new information may require that the hypothesis be modified. Clearly the accuracy of a prediction in any scientific study depends on the accuracy of the initial information on which it is based.

In our example, no great harm will come from an inaccurate prediction—that is, were we to find that some green apples are sweet. However, in some cases human life may depend on the accuracy of the prediction. For that and other reasons: (1) Repeated testing of scientific ideas is important, particularly because scientists working on the same problem do not always agree in their conclusions. (2) Careful observation is essential, even at the very outset of a study, because conclusions drawn from scientific tests are only as accurate as the information on which they are based.

A second criterion is that, even though hypotheses are guesses of a sort, *they must be based on measurable, describable facts. No mysticism can be theorized.* We cannot conjure up, to support our hypothesis, forces that have not been shown to exist. For example, as scientists, we cannot say that the tooth fairy took Johnny's tooth unless we can prove that the tooth fairy exists!

Third, a hypothesis *must not be anthropomorphic.* Human beings tend to anthropomorphize—that is, to relate all experiences to human experience. Whereas we could state that bears instinctively protect their young, it would be anthropomorphic to say that bears love their young, because love is a human emotional response. Thus, the initial hypothesis must be stated without interpretation.

Step 3: Data Collection

Once the initial hypothesis has been stated, scientists plan experiments that will provide data (or evidence) to support or disprove their hypotheses—that is, they *test* their hypotheses. They accumulate data by making qualitative or quantitative observations of some sort. The observations are often aided by the use of various types of equipment such as cameras, microscopes, stimulators, or various electronic devices that allow chemical and physiological measurements to be taken.

Observations referred to as **qualitative** are those we can make with our senses—that is, by using our vision, hearing, or sense of taste, smell, or touch. For some quick practice in qualitative observation, compare and contrast an orange and an apple. (*Compare* means to emphasize the similarities between two things, whereas *contrast* means to emphasize the differences.)

Whereas the differences between an apple and an orange are obvious, this is not always the case in biological observations. Quite often a scientist tries to detect very subtle differences that cannot be determined by qualitative observations; data must be derived from measurements. Such observations based on precise measurements of one type or another are **quantitative observations.** Examples of quantitative observations include careful measurements of body or organ dimensions such as mass, size, and volume; measurement of volumes of oxygen consumed during metabolic studies; determination of the concentration of glucose in urine; and determination of the differences in blood pressure and pulse under conditions of rest and exercise. An apple and an orange could be compared quantitatively by analyzing the relative amounts of sugar and water in a given volume of fruit flesh, the pigments and vitamins present in the apple skin and orange peel, and so on.

A valuable part of data gathering is the use of experiments to support or disprove a hypothesis. An **experiment** is a procedure designed to describe the factors in a given situation that affect one another (that is, to discover cause and effect) under certain conditions.

Two general rules govern experimentation. The first of these rules is that the experiment(s) should be conducted in such a manner that every **variable** (any factor that might affect the outcome of the experiment) is under the control of the experimenter. The **independent variables** are manipulated by the experimenter. For example, if the goal is to determine the effect of body temperature on breathing rate, the independent variable is body temperature. The effect observed or value measured (in this case breathing rate) is called the **dependent** or **response variable.** Its value "depends" on the value chosen for the independent variable. The ideal way to perform such an experiment is to set up and run a series of tests that are all identical, except for one specific factor that is varied.

One specimen (or group of specimens) is used as the **control** against which all other experimental samples are compared. The importance of the control sample cannot be overemphasized. The control group provides the "normal standard" against which all other samples are compared relative to the dependent variable. Taking our example one step further, if we wanted to investigate the effects of body temperature (the independent variable) on breathing rate (the dependent variable), we could collect data on the breathing rate of individuals with "normal" body temperature (the

implicit control group), and compare these data to breathing-rate measurements obtained from groups of individuals with higher and lower body temperatures.

The second rule governing experimentation is that valid results require that testing be done on large numbers of subjects. It is essential to understand that it is nearly impossible to control all possible variables in biological tests. Indeed, there is a bit of scientific wisdom that mirrors this truth—that is, that laboratory animals, even in the most rigidly controlled and carefully designed experiments, "will do as they damn well please." Thus, stating that the testing of a drug for its painkilling effects was successful after having tested it on only one postoperative patient would be scientific suicide. Large numbers of patients would have to receive the drug and be monitored for a decrease in postoperative pain before such a statement could have any scientific validity. Then, other researchers would have to be able to uphold those conclusions by running similar experiments. *Repeatability* is an important part of the scientific method and is the primary basis for support or rejection of many hypotheses.

During experimentation and observation, data must be carefully recorded. Usually, such initial, or raw, data are recorded in table form. The table should be labeled to show the variables investigated and the results for each sample. At this point, *accurate recording* of observations is the primary concern. Later, these raw data will be reorganized and manipulated to show more explicitly the outcome of the experimentation.

Some of the observations that you will be asked to make in the anatomy and physiology laboratory will require that a drawing be made. Don't panic! The purpose of making drawings (in addition to providing a record) is to force you to observe things very closely. You need not be an artist (most biological drawings are simple outline drawings), but you do need to be neat and as accurate as possible. It is advisable to use a 4H pencil to do your drawings because it is easily erased and doesn't smudge. Before beginning to draw, you should examine your specimen closely, studying it as though you were going to have to draw it from memory. For example, when looking at cells you should ask yourself questions such as "What is their shape—the relationship of length and width? How are they joined together?" Then decide precisely what you are going to show and how large the drawing must be to show the necessary detail. After making the drawing, add labels in the margins and connect them by straight lines (leader lines) to the structures being named.

Step 4: Manipulation and Analysis of Data

The form of the final data varies, depending on the nature of the data collected. Usually, the final data represent information converted from the original measured values (raw data) to some other form. This may mean that averaging or some other statistical treatment must be applied, or it may require conversions from one kind of units to another. In other cases, graphs may be needed to display the data.

Elementary Treatment of Data

Only very elementary statistical treatment of data is required in this manual. For example, you will be expected to understand and/or compute an average (mean), percentages, and a range.

Two of these statistics, the mean and the range, are useful in describing the *typical* case among a large number of samples evaluated. Let us use a simple example. We will assume that the following heart rates (in beats/min) were recorded during an experiment: 64, 70, 82, 94, 85, 75, 72, 78. If you put these numbers in numerical order, the **range** is easily computed, because the range is the difference between the highest and lowest numbers obtained (highest number minus lowest number). The **mean** is obtained by summing the items and dividing the sum by the number of items. What is the range and the mean for the set of numbers just provided?

1. _____*

The word *percent* comes from the Latin meaning "for 100"; thus *percent,* indicated by the percent sign, %, means parts per 100 parts. Thus, if we say that 45% of Americans have type O blood, what we are really saying is that among each group of 100 Americans, 45 (45/100) can be expected to have type O blood. Any ratio can be converted to a percent by multiplying by 100 and adding the percent sign.

$$.25 \times 100 = 25\% \qquad 5 \times 100 = 500\%$$

It is very easy to convert any number (including decimals) to a percent. The rule is to move the decimal point two places to the right and add the percent sign. If no decimal point appears, it is *assumed* to be at the end of the number; and zeros are added to fill any empty spaces. Two examples follow:

$$0.25 = 0.25 = 25\%$$
$$5 = 5 = 500\%$$

Change the following to percents:

2. 38 = _____   4. 1.6 = _____

3. .75 = _____

Note that although you are being asked here to convert numbers to percents, percents by themselves are meaningless. We always speak in terms of a percentage *of* something.

To change a percent to decimal form, remove the percent sign, and divide by 100. Change the following percents to whole numbers or decimals:

5. 800% = _____   6. 0.05% = _____

Making and Reading Line Graphs

For some laboratory experiments you will be required to show your data (or part of them) graphically. Simple line graphs allow relationships within the data to be shown interestingly and allow trends (or patterns) in the data to be demonstrated. An advantage of properly drawn graphs is that they save the reader's time because the essential meaning of a large amount of statistical data can be seen at a glance.

To aid in making accurate graphs, graph paper (or a printed grid in the manual) is used. Line graphs have both horizontal (X) and vertical (Y) axes with scales. Each scale

*Answers are given at the end of this section.

should have uniform intervals—that is, each unit measured on the scale should require the same distance along the scale as any other. Variations from this rule may be misleading and result in false interpretations of the data. By convention, the condition that is manipulated (the independent variable) in the experimental series is plotted on the X-axis (the horizontal axis); and the value that we then measure (the dependent variable) is plotted on the Y-axis (the vertical axis). To plot the data, a dot or a small x is placed at the precise point where the two variables (measured for each sample) meet; and then a line (this is called the **curve**) is drawn to connect the plotted points.

Sometimes, you will see the curve on a line graph extended beyond the last plotted point. This is (supposedly) done to predict "what comes next." When you see this done, be skeptical. The information provided by such a technique is only slightly more accurate than that provided by a crystal ball! When constructing a graph, be sure to label the X-axis and Y-axis and give the graph a legend (**Figure G.1**).

To read a line graph, pick any point on the line, and match it with the information directly below on the X-axis and with that directly to the left of it on the Y-axis. The figure below (Figure G.1) is a graph that illustrates the relationship between breaths per minute (respiratory rate) and body temperature. Answer the following questions about this graph:

7. What was the respiratory rate at a body temperature of

96°F? _____

8. Between which two body temperature readings was the

increase in breaths per minute greatest? _____

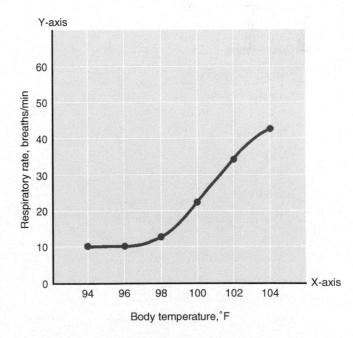

**Figure G.1 Example of graphically presented data.
Respiratory rate as a function of body temperature.**
Credit: Imagineering STA Media Services.

Step 5: Reporting Conclusions of the Study

Drawings, tables, and graphs alone do not suffice as the final presentation of scientific results. The final step requires that you provide a straightforward description of the conclusions drawn from your results. If possible, your findings should be compared to those of other investigators working on the same problem. For laboratory investigations conducted by students, these comparative figures are provided by classmates.

It is important to realize that scientific investigations do not always yield the anticipated results. If there are discrepancies between your results and those of others, or what you expected to find based on your class notes or textbook readings, this is the place to try to explain those discrepancies.

Results are often only as good as the observation techniques used. Depending on the type of experiment conducted, you may need to answer several questions. Did you weigh the specimen carefully enough? Did you balance the scale first? Was the subject's blood pressure actually as high as you recorded it, or did you record it inaccurately? If you did record it accurately, is it possible that the subject was emotionally upset about something, which might have given falsely high data for the variable being investigated? Attempting to explain an unexpected result will often teach you more than you would have learned from anticipated results.

When the experiment produces results that are consistent with the hypothesis, then the hypothesis can be said to have reached a higher level of certainty. The probability that the hypothesis is correct is greater.

A hypothesis that has been validated by many different investigators is called a **theory.** Theories are useful in two important ways. First, they link sets of data; and second, they make predictions that may lead to additional avenues of investigation. (OK, we know this with a high degree of certainty; what's next?)

When a theory has been repeatedly verified and appears to have wide applicability in biology, it may assume the status of a **biological principle.** A principle is a statement that applies with a high degree of probability to a range of events. For example, "Living matter is made of cells or cell products" is a principle stated in many biology texts. It is a sound and useful principle, and will continue to be used as such—unless new findings prove it wrong.

We have been through quite a bit of background concerning the scientific method and what its use entails. Because it is important that you remember the phases of the scientific method, they are summarized here:

1. Observation of some phenomenon

2. Statement of a hypothesis (based on the observations)

3. Collection of data (testing the hypothesis with controlled experiments)

4. Manipulation and analysis of the data

5. Reporting of the conclusions of the study (routinely done by preparing a lab report)

Lab Report

Cover Page

- Title of Experiment
- Author's Name
- Course
- Instructor
- Date

Introduction

- Provide background information.
- Describe any relevant observations.
- State hypotheses clearly.

Materials and Methods

- List equipment or supplies needed.
- Provide step-by-step directions for conducting the experiment.

Results

- Present data using a drawing (figure), table, or graph.
- Analyze data.
- Summarize findings briefly.

Discussion and Conclusions

- Conclude whether data gathered support or do not support hypotheses.
- Include relevant information from other sources.
- Explain any uncontrolled variables or unexpected difficulties.
- Make suggestions for further experimentation.

Reference List

- Cite the source of any material used to support this report.

Writing a Lab Report Based on the Scientific Method

A laboratory report is not the same as a scientific paper, but it has some of the same elements and is a formal way to report the results of a scientific experiment. The report should have a cover page that includes the title of the experiment, the author's name, the name of the course, the instructor, and the date. The report should include five separate, clearly marked sections: Introduction, Materials and Methods, Results, Discussion and Conclusions, and References. Use the previous template to guide you through writing a lab report.

Metrics

No matter how highly developed our ability to observe, observations have scientific value only if we can communicate them to others. Without measurement, we would be limited to qualitative description. For precise and repeatable communication of information, the agreed-upon system of measurement used by scientists is the **metric system.**

A major advantage of the metric system is that it is based on units of 10. This allows rapid conversion to workable numbers so that neither very large nor very small figures need be used in calculations. Fractions or multiples of the standard units of length, volume, mass, time, and temperature have been assigned specific names. The metric system (**Table G.1**) shows the commonly used units of the metric system, along with the prefixes used to designate fractions and multiples thereof.

To change from smaller units to larger units, you must *divide* by the appropriate factor of 10 (because there are fewer of the larger units). For example, a milliunit (*milli* = one-thousandth), such as a millimeter, is one step smaller than a centiunit (*centi* = one-hundredth), such as a centimeter. Thus to change milliunits to centiunits, you must divide by 10. On the other hand, when converting from larger units to smaller ones, you must *multiply* by the appropriate factor of 10. A partial scheme for conversions between the metric units is shown at the top of the next page.

The objectives of the sections that follow are to provide a brief overview of the most-used measurements in science or health professions and to help you gain some measure of confidence in dealing with them. A listing of the most frequently used conversion factors, for conversions between British and metric system units, is provided on the inside back cover.

Length Measurements

The metric unit of length is the **meter (m).** Smaller objects are measured in centimeters or millimeters. Subcellular structures are measured in micrometers.

To help you picture these units of length, some equivalents follow:

One meter (m) is slightly longer than one yard (1 m = 39.37 in.).

One centimeter (cm) is approximately the width of a piece of chalk. (Note: There are 2.54 cm in 1 in.)

One millimeter (mm) is approximately the thickness of the wire of a paper clip or of a mark made by a No. 2 pencil lead.

One micrometer (μm) is extremely tiny and can be measured only microscopically.

Make the following conversions between metric units of length:

9. 12 cm = _____ mm

10. 2000 μm = _____ mm

Now, circle the answer that would make the most sense in each of the following statements:

11. A match (in a matchbook) is (0.3, 3, 30) cm long.

12. A standard-size American car is about 4 (mm, cm, m, km) long.

Table G.1	Metric System				
A. Commonly used units		**B. Fractions and their multiples**			
Measurement	**Unit**	**Fraction or multiple**	**Prefix**	**Symbol**	
Length	Meter (m)	10^6 one million	mega	M	
Volume	Liter (L; l with prefix)	10^3 one thousand	kilo	k	
Mass	Gram (g)	10^{-1} one-tenth	deci	d	
Time*	Second (s)	10^{-2} one-hundredth	centi	c	
Temperature	Degree Celsius (°C)	10^{-3} one-thousandth	milli	m	
		10^{-6} one-millionth	micro	μ	
		10^{-9} one-billionth	nano	n	

* The accepted standard for time is the second; and thus hours and minutes are used in scientific, as well as everyday, measurement of time. The only prefixes generally used are those indicating *fractional portions* of seconds—for example, millisecond and microsecond.

$$\text{microunit} \underset{\times 1000}{\overset{\div 1000}{\rightleftharpoons}} \text{milliunit} \underset{\times 10}{\overset{\div 10}{\rightleftharpoons}} \text{centiunit} \underset{\times 100}{\overset{\div 100}{\rightleftharpoons}} \text{unit} \underset{\times 1000}{\overset{\div 1000}{\rightleftharpoons}} \text{kilounit}$$

smallest $\rightleftharpoons$ largest

Volume Measurements

The metric unit of volume is the liter. A **liter** (l, or sometimes L, especially without a prefix) is slightly more than a quart (1 L = 1.057 quarts). Liquid volumes measured out for lab experiments are usually measured in milliliters (ml). (The terms *ml* and *cc,* cubic centimeter, are used interchangeably in laboratory and medical settings.)

To help you visualize metric volumes, the equivalents of some common substances follow:

A 12-oz can of soda is a little less than 360 ml.

A fluid ounce is about 30 (it's 29.57) ml (cc).

A teaspoon of vanilla is about 5 ml (cc).

Compute the following:

13. How many 5-ml injections can be prepared from 1 liter

of a medicine? _____

14. A 450-ml volume of alcohol is _____ L.

Mass Measurements

Although many people use the terms *mass* and *weight* interchangeably, this usage is inaccurate. **Mass** is the amount of matter in an object; and an object has a constant mass, regardless of where it is—that is, on earth, or in outer space. However, weight varies with gravitational pull; the greater the gravitational pull, the greater the weight. Thus, our astronauts are said to be weightless when in outer space, but they still have the same mass as they do on earth. (Astronauts are not *really* weightless. It is just that they and their surroundings are being pulled toward the earth at the same speed; and so, in reference to their environment, they appear to float.)

The metric unit of mass is the **gram (g)**. Medical dosages are usually prescribed in milligrams (mg) or micrograms (μg); and in the clinical agency, body weight (particularly of infants) is typically specified in kilograms (kg; 1 kg = 2.2 lb).

The following examples are provided to help you become familiar with the masses of some common objects:

Two aspirin tablets have a mass of approximately 1 g.

A nickel has a mass of 5 g.

The mass of an average woman (132 lb) is 60 kg.

Make the following conversions:

15. 300 g = _____ mg = _____ μg

16. 4000 μg = _____ mg = _____ g

17. A nurse must administer to her patient, Mrs. Smith, 5 mg of a drug per kg of body mass. Mrs. Smith weighs 140 lb. How many grams of the drug should the nurse administer to her patient?

_____ g

Temperature Measurements

In the laboratory and in the clinical agency, temperature is measured both in metric units (degrees Celsius, °C) and in British units (degrees Fahrenheit, °F). Thus it helps to be familiar with both temperature scales.

The temperatures of boiling and freezing water can be used to compare the two scales:

The freezing point of water is 0°C and 32°F.

The boiling point of water is 100°C and 212°F.

As you can see, the range from the freezing point to the boiling point of water on the Celsius scale is 100 degrees, whereas the comparable range on the Fahrenheit scale is 180 degrees. Hence, one degree on the Celsius scale represents a greater change in temperature. Normal body temperature is approximately 98.6°F or 37°C.

To convert from the Celsius scale to the Fahrenheit scale, the following equation is used:

$$°C = \frac{5(°F - 32)}{9}$$

To convert from the Fahrenheit scale to the Celsius scale, the following equation is used:

$$°F = (9/5\ °C) + 32$$

Perform the following temperature conversions:

18. Convert 38°C to °F: _____

19. Convert 158°F to °C: _____

Answers

1. range of 94–64 or 30 beats/min; mean 77.5 **2.** 3800% **3.** 75% **4.** 160% **5.** 8 **6.** 0.0005 **7.** 10 breaths/min
8. interval between 100–102° (went from 22 to 36 breaths/min) **9.** 12 cm = 120 mm **10.** 2000 μm = 2 mm **11.** 3 cm long
12. 4 m long **13.** 200 **14.** 0.45 L **15.** 300 g = 3×10^5 mg = 3×10^8 μg **16.** 4000 μg = $\underline{4}$ mg = 4×10^{-3} g (0.004 g)
17. 0.32 g **18.** 100.4°F **19.** 70°C

Anatomy and Physiology Laboratory Safety Guidelines*

1. Upon entering the laboratory, locate exits, fire extinguisher, fire blanket, chemical shower, eyewash station, first aid kit, containers for broken glass, and materials for cleaning up spills.

2. Do not eat, drink, smoke, handle contact lenses, store food, or apply cosmetics or lip balm in the laboratory. Restrain long hair, loose clothing, and dangling jewelry.

3. Students who are pregnant, are taking immunosuppressive drugs, or have any other medical conditions (e.g., diabetes, immunological defect) that might necessitate special precautions in the laboratory must inform the instructor immediately.

4. Wearing contact lenses in the laboratory is inadvisable because they do not provide eye protection and may trap material on the surface of the eye. Soft contact lenses may absorb volatile chemicals. If possible, wear regular eyeglasses instead.

5. Use safety glasses in all experiments involving liquids, aerosols, vapors, and gases.

6. Decontaminate work surfaces at the beginning and end of every lab period, using a commercially prepared disinfectant or 10% bleach solution. After labs involving dissection of preserved material, use hot soapy water or disinfectant.

7. Keep all liquids away from the edge of the lab bench to avoid spills. Clean up spills of viable materials using disinfectant or 10% bleach solution.

8. Properly label glassware and slides.

9. Use mechanical pipetting devices; mouth pipetting is prohibited.

10. Wear disposable gloves when handling blood and other body fluids, mucous membranes, and nonintact skin, and when touching items or surfaces soiled with blood or other body fluids. Change gloves between procedures. Wash hands immediately after removing gloves. (**Note:** Cover open cuts or scrapes with a sterile bandage before donning gloves.)

11. Place glassware and plasticware contaminated by blood and other body fluids in a disposable autoclave bag for decontamination by autoclaving, or place them directly into a 10% bleach solution before reuse or disposal. Place disposable materials such as gloves, mouthpieces, swabs, and toothpicks that have come into contact with body fluids into a disposable autoclave bag, and decontaminate before disposal.

12. To help prevent contamination by needlestick injuries, use only disposable needles and lancets. Do not bend the needles and lancets. Needles and lancets should be placed promptly in a labeled, puncture-resistant, leakproof container and decontaminated, preferably by autoclaving.

13. Do not leave heat sources unattended.

14. Report all spills or accidents, no matter how minor, to the instructor.

15. Never work alone in the laboratory.

16. Remove protective clothing before leaving the laboratory.

---

*Adapted from:

Biosafety in Microbiological and Biomedical Laboratories (BMBL), Fifth Edition. 2007. U.S. Government Printing Office. Washington, D.C. www.cdc.gov/od/OHS/biosfty/bmbl5/bmbl5toc.htm

Centers for Disease Control. 1996. "Universal Precautions for Prevention of Transmission of HIV and Other Bloodborne Infections." Washington, D.C. www.cdc.gov/ncidod/dhqp/bp_universal_precautions.html

Johnson, Ted, and Christine Case. 2010. *Laboratory Experiments in Microbiology*, Ninth Edition. San Francisco: Pearson Benjamin Cummings.

School Chemistry Laboratory Safety Guide. 2006. U.S. Consumer Product Safety Commission. Bethesda, MD. www.cpsc.gov/CPSCPUB/PUBS/NIOSH2007107.pdf

The Metric System

Measurement	Unit and abbreviation	Metric equivalent	Metric to English conversion factor	English to metric conversion factor
Length	1 kilometer (km) 1 meter (m)	= 1000 (10^3) meters = 100 (10^2) centimeters = 1000 millimeters	1 km = 0.62 mile 1 m = 1.09 yards 1 m = 3.28 feet 1 m = 39.37 inches	1 mile = 1.61 km 1 yard = 0.914 m 1 foot = 0.305 m 1 foot = 30.5 cm
	1 centimeter (cm)	= 0.01 (10^{-2}) meter	1 cm = 0.394 inch 1 mm = 0.039 inch	1 inch = 2.54 cm
	1 millimeter (mm)	= 0.001 (10^{-3}) meter		
	1 micrometer (μm) [formerly micron (μ)]	= 0.000001 (10^{-6}) meter		
	1 nanometer (nm) [formerly millimicron (mμ)]	= 0.000000001 (10^{-9}) meter		
	1 angstrom (Å)	= 0.0000000001 (10^{-10}) meter		
Area	1 square meter (m²)	= 10,000 square centimeters	1 m² = 1.1960 square yards 1 m² = 10.764 square feet	1 square yard = 0.8361 m² 1 square foot = 0.0929 m²
	1 square centimeter (cm²)	= 100 square millimeters	1 cm² = 0.155 square inch	1 square inch = 6.4516 cm²
Mass	1 metric ton (t) 1 kilogram (kg) 1 gram (g)	= 1000 kilograms = 1000 grams = 1000 milligrams	1 t = 1.103 ton 1 kg = 2.205 pounds 1 g = 0.0353 ounce 1 g = 15.432 grains	1 ton = 0.907 t 1 pound = 0.4536 kg 1 ounce = 28.35 g
	1 milligram (mg)	= 0.001 gram	1 mg = approx. 0.015 grain	
	1 microgram (μg)	= 0.000001 gram		
Volume (solids)	1 cubic meter (m³)	= 1,000,000 cubic centimeters	1 m³ = 1.3080 cubic yards 1 m³ = 35.315 cubic feet	1 cubic yard = 0.7646 m³ 1 cubic foot = 0.0283 m³
	1 cubic centimeter (cm³ or cc) 1 cubic millimeter (mm³)	= 0.000001 cubic meter = 1 milliliter = 0.000000001 cubic meter	1 cm³ = 0.0610 cubic inch	1 cubic inch = 16.387 cm³
Volume (liquids and gases)	1 kiloliter (kl or kL) 1 liter (l or L)	= 1000 liters = 1000 milliliters	1 kL = 264.17 gallons 1 L = 0.264 gallons 1 L = 1.057 quarts	1 gallon = 3.785 L 1 quart = 0.946 L
	1 milliliter (ml or mL)	= 0.001 liter = 1 cubic centimeter	1 ml = 0.034 fluid ounce 1 ml = approx. $\frac{1}{4}$ teaspoon 1 ml = approx. 15–16 drops (gtt.)	1 quart = 946 ml 1 pint = 473 ml 1 fluid ounce = 29.57 ml 1 teaspoon = approx. 5 ml
	1 microliter (μl or μL)	= 0.000001 liter		
Time	1 second (s or sec) 1 millisecond (ms or msec)	= $\frac{1}{60}$ minute = 0.001 second		
Temperature	Degrees Celsius (°C)		$°F = \frac{9}{5}(°C) + 32$	$°C = \frac{5}{9}(°F - 32)$

Surface Anatomy Roundup

Learning Outcomes

▶ Define *surface anatomy*, and explain why it is an important field of study; define *palpation*.

▶ Describe and palpate the major surface features of the cranium, face, and neck.

▶ Describe the easily palpated bony and muscular landmarks of the back, and locate the vertebral spines on the living body.

▶ List the bony surface landmarks of the thoracic cage, explain how they relate to the major soft organs of the thorax, and explain how to find the second to eleventh ribs.

▶ Name and palpate the important surface features on the anterior abdominal wall, and explain how to palpate a full bladder.

▶ Define and explain the following: *linea alba, umbilical hernia*, examination for an inguinal hernia, *linea semilunaris*, and *McBurney's point*.

▶ Locate and palpate the main surface features of the upper limb.

▶ Explain the significance of the cubital fossa, pulse points in the distal forearm, and the anatomical snuff box.

▶ Describe and palpate the surface landmarks of the lower limb.

▶ Explain exactly where to administer an injection in the gluteal region and in the other major sites of intramuscular injection.

Go to Mastering A&P™ > **Study Area to improve your performance in A&P Lab.**

> **Lab Tools** > **Practice Anatomy Lab** > **Anatomical Models**

Instructors may assign new Building Vocabulary coaching activities, Pre-Lab Quiz questions, Art Labeling activities, Practice Anatomy Lab Practical questions (PAL), and more using the Mastering A&P™ Item Library.

Materials

▶ Articulated skeletons
▶ Three-dimensional models or charts of the skeletal muscles of the body
▶ Hand mirror
▶ Stethoscope
▶ Alcohol swabs
▶ Washable markers

Pre-Lab Quiz

Instructors may assign these and other Pre-Lab Quiz questions using Mastering A&P™

1. The epicranial aponeurosis binds to the subcutaneous tissue of the cranium to form the:
   a. mastoid process
   b. occipital protuberance
   c. true scalp
   d. xiphoid process

2. The _____ is the most prominent neck muscle and also the neck's most important landmark.
   a. buccinator
   b. epicranius
   c. masseter
   d. sternocleidomastoid

3. The three boundaries of the _____ are the trapezius medially, the latissimus dorsi inferiorly, and the scapula laterally.
   a. torso triangle
   b. triangle of ausculation
   c. triangle of back muscles
   d. triangle of McBurney

4. Circle True or False. With the exception of a full bladder, most internal pelvic organs are not easily palpated through the skin of the body surface.

5. On the dorsal surface of your hand is a grouping of superficial veins known as the _____, which provides a site for drawing blood and inserting intravenous catheters.
   a. anatomical snuff box
   b. dorsal venous network
   c. radial and ulnar veins
   d. palmar arches

From Exercise 46 of *Human Anatomy & Physiology Laboratory Manual*, Twelfth Edition. Elaine N. Marieb, Lori A. Smith.

Surface anatomy is a valuable branch of anatomical and medical science. True to its name, **surface anatomy** does indeed study the *external surface* of the body, but more important, it also studies *internal* organs as they relate to external surface landmarks and as they are seen and felt through the skin. Feeling internal structures through the skin with the fingers is called **palpation** (literally, "touching").

Surface anatomy is living anatomy, better studied in live people than in cadavers. It can provide a great deal of information about the living skeleton (almost all bones can be palpated) and about the muscles and blood vessels that lie near the body surface. Furthermore, a skilled examiner can learn a good deal about the heart, lungs, and other deep organs by performing a surface assessment. Thus, surface anatomy serves as the basis of the standard physical examination. If you are planning a career in the health sciences or physical education, a study of surface anatomy will show you where to take pulses, where to insert tubes and needles, where to locate broken bones and inflamed muscles, and where to listen for the sounds of the lungs, heart, and intestines.

We will take a regional approach to surface anatomy, exploring the head first and proceeding to the trunk and the limbs. You will be observing and palpating your own body as you work through the exercise, because your body is the best learning tool of all. To aid your exploration of living anatomy, skeletons and muscle models or charts are provided around the lab so that you can review the bones and muscles you will encounter. Whenever possible, have a study partner assume the role of the subject for skin sites that you cannot reach on your own body.

Activity 1

Palpating Landmarks of the Head

The head (**Figure 1** and **Figure 2**) is divided into the cranium and the face.

Cranium

1. Run your fingers over the superior surface of your head. Notice that the underlying cranial bones lie very near the surface. Proceed to your forehead and palpate the **superciliary arches** (brow ridges) directly superior to your orbits (Figure 1).

2. Move your hand to the posterior surface of your skull, where you can feel the knoblike **external occipital protuberance**. Run your finger directly laterally from this projection to feel the ridgelike *superior nuchal line* on the occipital bone. This line, which marks the superior extent of the muscles of the posterior neck, serves as the boundary between the head and the neck. Now feel the prominent **mastoid process** on each side of the cranium just posterior to your ear.

3. The **frontal belly** of the epicranius (Figure 2) inserts superiorly onto the broad aponeurosis called the *epicranial aponeurosis* that covers the superior surface of the cranium. This aponeurosis binds tightly to the overlying subcutaneous tissue and skin to form the true **scalp**. Push on your scalp, and confirm that it slides freely over the underlying cranial bones. Because the scalp is only loosely bound to the skull, people can easily be "scalped" (in industrial accidents, for example). The scalp is richly vascularized by a large number of arteries running through its subcutaneous tissue. Most arteries of the body constrict and close after they are cut or torn, but those in the scalp are unable to do so because they are held open by the dense connective tissue surrounding them.

What do these facts suggest about the amount of bleeding that accompanies scalp wounds?

_____

_____

Face

The surface of the face is divided into many different regions, including the *orbital*, *nasal*, *oral* (mouth), and *auricular* (ear) areas.

1. Trace a finger around the entire margin of the bony orbit. The **lacrimal fossa**, which contains the tear-gathering lacrimal sac, may be felt on the medial side of the eye socket.

2. Touch the most superior part of your nose, its **root**, which lies between the eyebrows (Figure 2). Just inferior to this, between your eyes, is the **bridge** of the nose formed by the nasal bones. Continue your finger's progress inferiorly along the nose's anterior margin, the **dorsum nasi**, to the tip of the nose, the **apex**. Place one finger in a nostril and another finger on the flared winglike **ala** that defines the nostril's lateral border.

3. Grasp your **auricle**, the shell-like part of the external ear that surrounds the opening of the **external acoustic meatus** (Figure 1). Now trace the ear's outer rim, or **helix**, to the **lobule** (earlobe) inferiorly. The lobule is easily pierced, and since it is not highly sensitive to pain, it provides a convenient place to hang an earring or obtain a drop of blood for clinical blood analysis. Next, place a finger on your temple just anterior to the auricle.

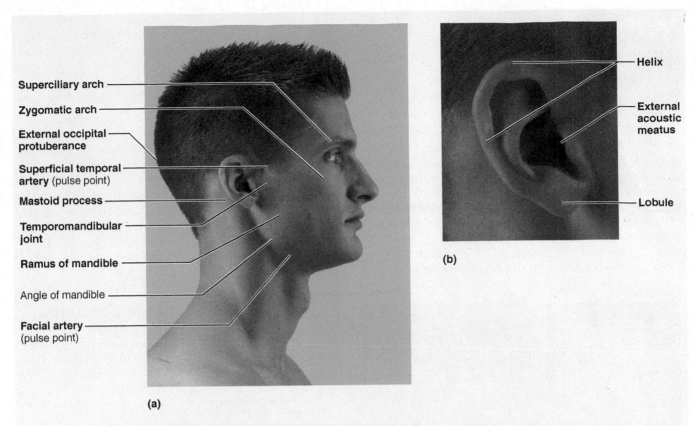

Superciliary arch

Zygomatic arch

External occipital protuberance

Superficial temporal artery (pulse point)

Mastoid process

Temporomandibular joint

Ramus of mandible

Angle of mandible

Facial artery (pulse point)

Helix

External acoustic meatus

Lobule

(b)

(a)

Figure 1 Surface anatomy of the head. (a) Lateral aspect. **(b)** Close-up of an auricle.

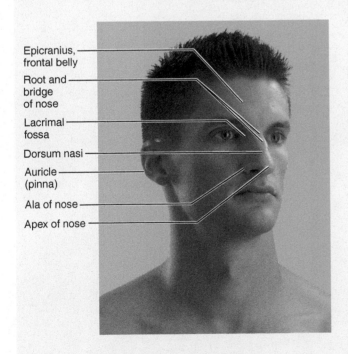

Epicranius, frontal belly

Root and bridge of nose

Lacrimal fossa

Dorsum nasi

Auricle (pinna)

Ala of nose

Apex of nose

Figure 2 Surface structures of the face.

There, you may be able to feel the pulsations of the **superficial temporal artery**, which ascends to supply the scalp (Figure 1).

4. Run your hand anteriorly from your ear toward the orbit, and feel the **zygomatic arch** just deep to the skin. This bony arch is easily broken by blows to the face. Next, place your fingers on the skin of your face, and feel it bunch and stretch as you contort your face into smiles, frowns, and grimaces. You are now monitoring the action of several of the subcutaneous **muscles of facial expression**.

5. On your lower jaw, palpate the parts of the bony **mandible**: its anterior body and its posterior ascending **ramus**. Press on the skin over the mandibular ramus, and feel the **masseter muscle** bulge when you clench your teeth. Palpate the anterior border of the masseter, and trace it to the mandible's inferior margin. At this point, you will be able to detect the pulse of your **facial artery** (Figure 1). Finally, to feel the **temporomandibular joint**, place a finger directly anterior to the external acoustic meatus of your ear, and open and close your mouth several times. The bony structure you feel moving is the *condylar process of the mandible*.

Activity 2

Palpating Landmarks of the Neck

Bony Landmarks

1. Run your fingers inferiorly along the back of your neck, in the posterior midline, to feel the *spinous processes* of the cervical vertebrae. The spine of C₇, the *vertebra prominens*, is especially prominent.

2. Now, beginning at your chin, run a finger inferiorly along the anterior midline of your neck (**Figure 3**). The first hard structure you encounter will be the U-shaped **hyoid bone**, which lies in the angle between the floor of the mouth and the vertical part of the neck. Directly inferior to this, you will feel the **laryngeal prominence** (Adam's apple) of the thyroid cartilage. Just inferior to the laryngeal prominence, your finger will sink into a soft depression (formed by the **cricothyroid ligament**) before

proceeding onto the rounded surface of the **cricoid cartilage**. Now swallow several times, and feel the whole larynx move up and down.

3. Continue inferiorly to the trachea. Attempt to palpate the *isthmus of the thyroid gland*, which feels like a spongy cushion over the second to fourth tracheal rings (Figure 3). Then, try to palpate the two soft lateral *lobes* of your thyroid gland along the sides of the trachea.

4. Move your finger all the way inferiorly to the root of the neck, and rest it in the **jugular notch**, the depression in the superior part of the sternum between the two clavicles. By pushing deeply at this point, you can feel the cartilage rings of the trachea.

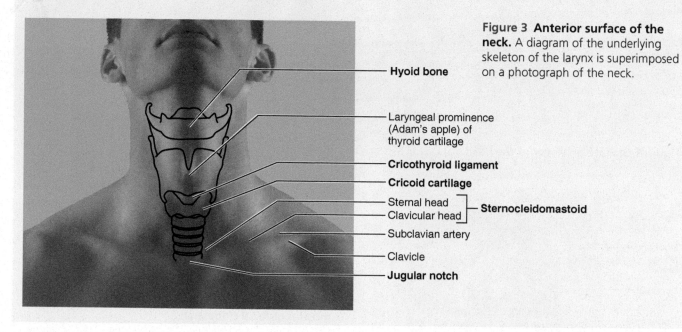

Figure 3 Anterior surface of the neck. A diagram of the underlying skeleton of the larynx is superimposed on a photograph of the neck.

Hyoid bone

Laryngeal prominence (Adam's apple) of thyroid cartilage

Cricothyroid ligament

Cricoid cartilage

Sternal head
Clavicular head — **Sternocleidomastoid**

Subclavian artery

Clavicle

Jugular notch

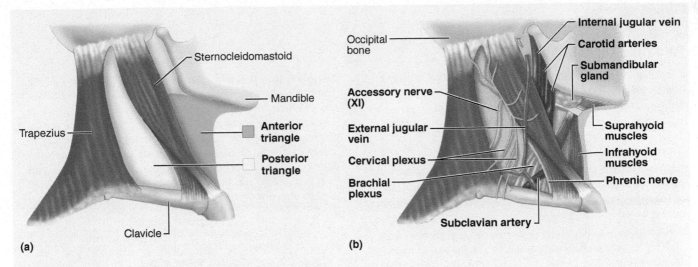

Figure 4 Anterior and posterior triangles of the neck. (a) Boundaries of the triangles. **(b)** Some contents of the triangles.

Muscles

The **sternocleidomastoid** is the most prominent muscle in the neck and the neck's most important surface landmark. You can best see and feel it when you turn your head to the side.

Obtain a hand mirror, hold it in front of your face, and turn your head sharply from right to left several times. You will be able to see both heads of this muscle, the **sternal head** medially and the **clavicular head** laterally (Figure 3). Several important structures lie beside or beneath the sternocleidomastoid:

- The *cervical lymph nodes* lie both superficial and deep to this muscle. Swollen cervical nodes provide evidence of infections or cancer of the head and neck.

- The *common carotid artery* and *internal jugular vein* lie just deep to the sternocleidomastoid, a relatively superficial location that exposes these vessels to danger in slashing wounds to the neck.

- Just lateral to the inferior part of the sternocleidomastoid is the large **subclavian artery** on its way to supply the upper limb. By pushing on the subclavian artery at this point, one can stop the bleeding from a wound anywhere in the associated limb.

- Just anterior to the sternocleidomastoid, superior to the level of your larynx, you can feel a carotid pulse—the pulsations of the **external carotid artery (Figure 4)**.

- The *external jugular vein* descends vertically, just superficial to the sternocleidomastoid and deep to the skin (Figure 4b). To make this vein "appear" on your neck, stand before the mirror, and gently compress the skin superior to your clavicle with your fingers.

Triangles of the Neck

The sternocleidomastoid muscles divide each side of the neck into the posterior and anterior triangles (Figure 4a).

1. The **posterior triangle** is defined by the sternocleidomastoid anteriorly, the trapezius posteriorly, and the clavicle inferiorly. Palpate the borders of the posterior triangle.

The **anterior triangle** is defined by the inferior margin of the mandible superiorly, the midline of the neck anteriorly, and the sternocleidomastoid posteriorly.

2. The contents of these two triangles include nerves, glands, blood vessels, and small muscles (Figure 4b). The posterior triangle contains the **accessory nerve** (cranial nerve XI), most of the **cervical plexus**, and the **phrenic nerve**. In the inferior part of the triangle are the **external jugular vein**, the trunks of the **brachial plexus**, and the **subclavian artery**. These structures are relatively superficial and are easily cut or injured by wounds to the neck.

In the neck's anterior triangle, important structures include the **submandibular gland**, the **suprahyoid** and **infrahyoid muscles**, and parts of the **carotid arteries** and **jugular veins** that lie superior to the sternocleidomastoid.

- Palpate your carotid pulse.

A wound to the posterior triangle of the neck can lead to long-term loss of sensation in the skin of the neck and shoulder, as well as partial paralysis of the sternocleidomastoid and trapezius muscles. Explain these effects. ✚

_____

_____

Activity 3

Palpating Landmarks of the Trunk

The trunk of the body consists of the thorax, abdomen, pelvis, and perineum. The *back* includes parts of all of these regions, but for convenience it is treated separately.

The Back

Bones

1. The vertical groove in the center of the back is called the **posterior median furrow (Figure 5)**. The *spinous processes* of the vertebrae are visible in the furrow when the spinal column is flexed.

- Palpate a few of these processes on your partner's back (C_7 and T_1 are the most prominent and the easiest to find).

- Also palpate the posterior parts of some ribs, as well as the prominent **spine of the scapula** and the scapula's long **medial border**.

   The scapula lies superficial to ribs 2 to 7; its **inferior angle** is at the level of the spinous process of vertebra T_7. The medial end of the scapular spine lies opposite the T_3 spinous process.

2. Now feel the **iliac crests** (superior margins of the iliac bones) in your own lower back. You can find these crests effortlessly by resting your hands on your hips. Locate the most superior point of each crest, a point that lies roughly halfway between the posterior median furrow and the lateral side of the body (Figure 5). A horizontal line through these two superior points, the **supracristal line**, intersects L_4, providing a simple way to locate that vertebra. The ability to locate L_4 is essential for performing a *lumbar puncture*, a procedure in which the clinician inserts a needle into the vertebral canal of the spinal column directly superior or inferior to L_4 and withdraws cerebrospinal fluid.

3. The *sacrum* is easy to palpate just superior to the cleft in the buttocks. You can feel the *coccyx* in the extreme inferior part of that cleft, just posterior to the anus.

Muscles

The largest superficial muscles of the back are the **trapezius** superiorly and **latissimus dorsi** inferiorly (Figure 5). Furthermore, the deeper **erector spinae** muscles are very evident in the lower back, flanking the vertebral column like thick vertical cords.

1. Shrug your shoulders to feel the trapezius contracting just deep to the skin.

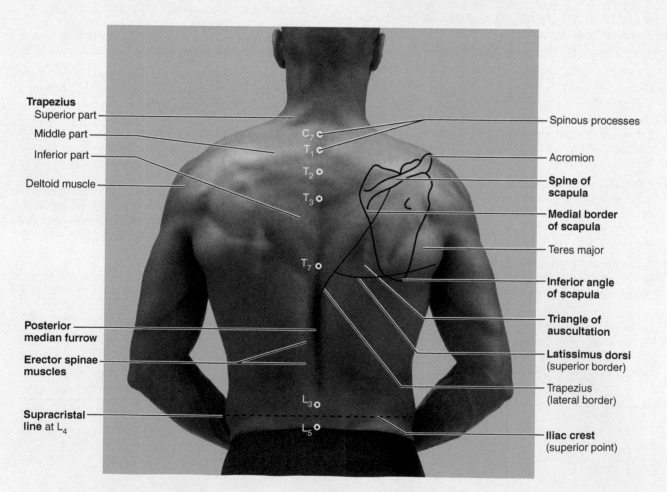

Figure 5 Surface anatomy of the back.

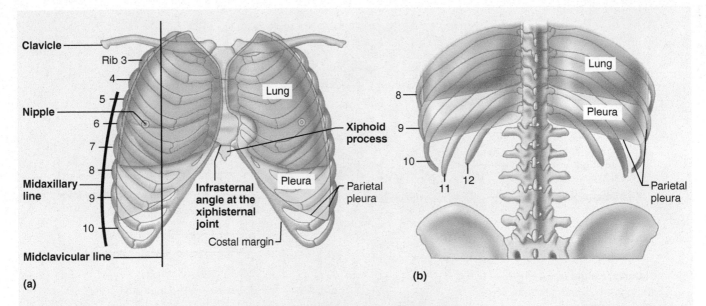

Figure 6 The bony rib cage as it relates to the underlying lungs and pleural cavities. Both the pleural cavities (blue) and the lungs (pink) are outlined. **(a)** Anterior view. **(b)** Posterior view.

2. Feel your partner's erector spinae muscles contract and bulge as he straightens his spine from a slightly bent-over position.

The superficial muscles of the back fail to cover a small area of the rib cage called the **triangle of auscultation** (Figure 5). This triangle lies just medial to the inferior part of the scapula. Its three boundaries are formed by the trapezius medially, the latissimus dorsi inferiorly, and the scapula laterally. The physician places a stethoscope over the skin of this triangle to listen for lung sounds (*auscultation* = listening). To hear the lungs clearly, the doctor first asks the patient to fold the arms together in front of the chest and then flex the trunk.

What do you think is the precise reason for having the patient take this action?

_____

_____

3. Have your partner assume the position just described. After cleaning the earpieces with an alcohol swab, use the stethoscope to auscultate the lung sounds. Compare the clarity of the lung sounds heard over the triangle of auscultation to that over other areas of the back.

The Thorax

Bones

1. Start exploring the anterior surface of your partner's bony *thoracic cage* (**Figure 6** and **Figure 7**) by defining the extent of the *sternum*. Use a finger to trace the sternum's triangular *manubrium* inferior to the jugular notch, its flat *body*, and the tongue-shaped **xiphoid process**. Now palpate the ridgelike **sternal angle**, where the manubrium meets the body of the sternum. Locating the sternal angle is important because it directs you to the second ribs (which attach to it). Once you find the second rib, you can count down to identify every other

rib in the thorax (except the first and sometimes the twelfth rib, which lie too deep to be palpated). The sternal angle is a highly reliable landmark—it is easy to locate, even in overweight people.

2. By locating the individual ribs, you can mentally "draw" a series of horizontal lines of "latitude" that you can use to map and locate the underlying visceral organs of the thoracic cavity. Such mapping also requires lines of "longitude," so let us construct some vertical lines on the wall of your partner's trunk. As he lifts an arm straight up in the air, extend a line inferiorly from the center of the axilla onto his lateral thoracic wall. This is the **midaxillary line** (Figure 6a). Now estimate the midpoint of his **clavicle**, and run a vertical line inferiorly from that point toward the groin. This is the **midclavicular line**, and it will pass about 1 cm medial to the nipple.

3. Next, feel along the V-shaped inferior edge of the rib cage, the **costal margin**. At the **infrasternal angle**, the superior angle of the costal margin, lies the **xiphisternal joint**. The heart lies on the diaphragm deep to the xiphisternal joint.

4. The thoracic cage provides many valuable landmarks for locating the vital organs of the thoracic and abdominal cavities. On the anterior thoracic wall, ribs 2–6 define the superior-to-inferior extent of the female breast, and the fourth intercostal space indicates the location of the **nipple** in men, children, and small-breasted women. The right costal margin runs across the anterior surface of the liver and gallbladder. Surgeons must be aware of the inferior margin of the *pleural cavities* because if they accidentally cut into one of these cavities, a lung collapses. The inferior pleural margin lies adjacent to vertebra T_{12} near the posterior midline (Figure 6b) and runs horizontally across the back to reach rib 10 at the midaxillary line. From there, the pleural margin ascends to rib 8 in the midclavicular line (Figure 6a) and to the level of the xiphisternal joint near the

Text continues on next page. ➔

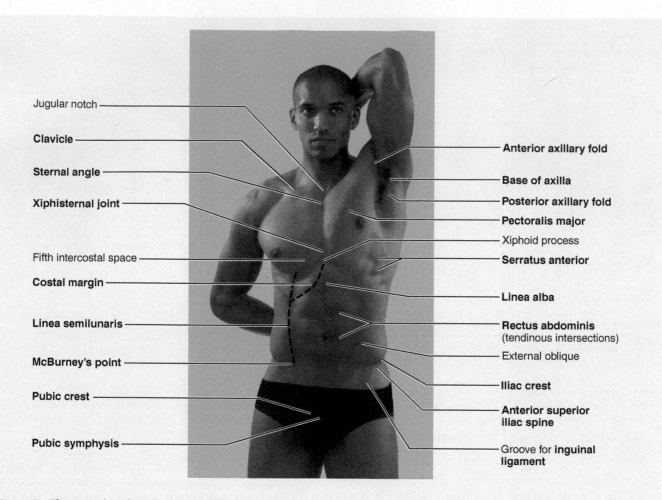

Figure 7 The anterior thorax and abdomen.

anterior midline. The *lungs* do not fill the inferior region of the pleural cavity. Instead, their inferior borders run at a level that is two ribs superior to the pleural margin, until they meet that margin near the xiphisternal joint.

5. Let's review the relationship of the *heart* to the thoracic cage. The superior right corner of the heart lies at the junction of the third rib and the sternum; the superior left corner lies at the second rib, near the sternum; the inferior left corner lies in the fifth intercostal space in the midclavicular line; and the inferior right corner lies at the sternal border of the sixth rib. You may wish to outline the heart on your chest or that

of your lab partner by connecting the four corner points with a washable marker.

Muscles

The main superficial muscles of the anterior thoracic wall are the **pectoralis major** and the anterior slips of the **serratus anterior** (Figure 7).

• Palpate these two muscles on your chest. They both contract during push-ups, and you can confirm this by pushing yourself up from your desk with one arm while palpating the muscles with your opposite hand.

Activity 4

Palpating Landmarks of the Abdomen

Bony Landmarks

The anterior abdominal wall (Figure 7) extends inferiorly from the costal margin to an inferior boundary that is defined by several landmarks. Palpate these landmarks as they are described below.

1. **Iliac crest**. Locate the iliac crests by resting your hands on your hips.

2. **Anterior superior iliac spine**. Representing the most anterior point of the iliac crest, this spine is a prominent landmark. It can be palpated in everyone, even those who are overweight. Run your fingers anteriorly along the iliac crest to its end.

3. **Inguinal ligament**. The inguinal ligament, indicated by a groove on the skin of the groin, runs medially from the anterior superior iliac spine to the pubic tubercle of the pubis.

4. Pubic crest. You will have to press deeply to feel this crest on the pubis near the median **pubic symphysis**. The **pubic tubercle**, the most lateral point of the pubic crest, is easier to palpate, but you will still have to push deeply.

Inguinal hernias occur immediately superior to the inguinal ligament and may exit from a medial opening called the **superficial inguinal ring**. To locate this ring, one would palpate the pubic tubercle. An inguinal hernia in a male can be detected by pushing into the superficial inguinal ring **(Figure 8).** ✚

Muscles and Other Surface Features

The central landmark of the anterior abdominal wall is the *umbilicus* (navel). Running superiorly and inferiorly from the umbilicus is the **linea alba** ("white line"), represented in the skin of lean people by a vertical groove (Figure 7). The linea alba is a tendinous seam that extends from the xiphoid process to the pubic symphysis, just medial to the rectus abdominis muscles). The linea alba is a favored site for surgical entry into the abdominal cavity because the surgeon can make a long cut through this line with no muscle damage and minimal bleeding.

Several kinds of hernias involve the umbilicus and the linea alba. In an **acquired umbilical hernia**, the linea alba weakens until intestinal coils push through it just superior to the navel. The herniated coils form a bulge just deep to the skin.

Another type of umbilical hernia is a **congenital umbilical hernia**, present in some infants: The umbilical hernia is seen as a cherry-sized bulge deep to the skin of the navel that enlarges whenever the baby cries. Congenital umbilical hernias are usually harmless, and most correct themselves automatically before the child's second birthday. ✚

1. McBurney's point is the spot on the anterior abdominal skin that lies directly superficial to the base of the appendix (Figure 7). It is located one-third of the way along a line between the right anterior superior iliac spine and the umbilicus. Try to find it on your body.

McBurney's point is often the place where the pain of appendicitis is experienced most acutely. Pain at McBurney's point after the pressure is removed (rebound tenderness) can indicate appendicitis. This is not a *precise* method of diagnosis, however.

2. Flanking the linea alba are the vertical straplike **rectus abdominis** muscles (Figure 7). Feel these muscles contract just deep to your skin as you do a bent-knee sit-up (or as you bend forward after leaning back in your chair). In the skin of lean people, the lateral margin of each rectus muscle makes a groove known as the **linea semilunaris** (half-moon line). On your right side, estimate where your linea semilunaris crosses the costal margin of the rib cage. The *gallbladder* lies just deep to this spot, so this is the standard point of incision for gallbladder surgery. In muscular people, three horizontal grooves can be seen in the skin covering the rectus abdominis. These grooves represent the **tendinous intersections**, fibrous bands that subdivide the rectus muscle. Because of these subdivisions, each rectus abdominis muscle presents four distinct bulges. Try to identify these insertions on yourself or your partner.

3. The only other major muscles that can be seen or felt through the anterior abdominal wall are the lateral **external obliques**. Feel these muscles contract as you cough, strain, or raise your intra-abdominal pressure in some other way.

4. The anterior abdominal wall can be divided into four quadrants. A clinician listening to a patient's **bowel sounds** places the stethoscope over each of the four abdominal quadrants, one after another. Normal bowel sounds, which result as peristalsis moves air and fluid through the intestine, are high-pitched gurgles that occur every 5 to 15 seconds.

- Use the stethoscope to listen to your own or your partner's bowel sounds.

Abnormal bowel sounds can indicate intestinal disorders. Absence of bowel sounds indicates a halt in intestinal activity, which follows long-term obstruction of the intestine, surgical handling of the intestine, peritonitis, or other conditions. Loud tinkling or splashing sounds, by contrast, indicate an increase in intestinal activity. Such loud sounds may accompany gastroenteritis (inflammation and upset of the GI tract) or a partly obstructed intestine. ✚

The Pelvis and Perineum

The bony surface features of the *pelvis* are considered with the bony landmarks of the abdomen and the gluteal region. Most *internal* pelvic organs are not palpable through the skin of the body surface. A full *bladder*, however, becomes firm and can be felt through the abdominal wall just superior to the pubic symphysis. A bladder that can be palpated more than a few centimeters above this symphysis is retaining urine and dangerously full, and it should be drained by catheterization.

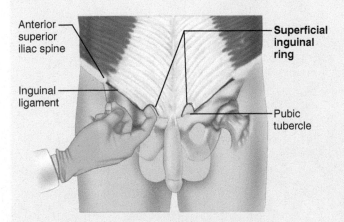

Figure 8 Clinical examination for an inguinal hernia in a male. The examiner palpates the patient's pubic tubercle, pushes superiorly to invaginate the scrotal skin into the superficial inguinal ring, and asks the patient to cough. If an inguinal hernia exists, it will push inferiorly and touch the examiner's fingertip.

Labels on figure: Anterior superior iliac spine; Inguinal ligament; Superficial inguinal ring; Pubic tubercle

Activity 5

Palpating Landmarks of the Upper Limb

Axilla

The **base of the axilla** is the groove in which the underarm hair grows (Figure 7). Deep to this base lie the axillary *lymph nodes* (which swell and can be palpated in breast cancer), the large *axillary vessels* serving the upper limb, and much of the brachial plexus. The base of the axilla forms a "valley" between two thick, rounded ridges, the **axillary folds**. Just anterior to the base, clutch your **anterior axillary fold**, formed by the pectoralis major muscle. Then grasp your **posterior axillary fold**. This fold is formed by the latissimus dorsi and teres major muscles of the back as they course toward their insertions on the humerus.

Shoulder

1. Again locate the prominent spine of the scapula posteriorly (Figure 5). Follow the spine to its lateral end, the flattened **acromion** on the shoulder's summit. Then, palpate the **clavicle** anteriorly, tracing this bone from the sternum to the shoulder (**Figure 9**). Notice the clavicle's curved shape.

2. Now locate the junction between the clavicle and the acromion on the superolateral surface of your shoulder, at the **acromioclavicular joint**. To find this joint, thrust your arm anteriorly repeatedly until you can palpate the precise point of pivoting action.

3. Next, place your fingers on the **greater tubercle** of the humerus. This is the most lateral bony landmark on the superior surface of the shoulder. It is covered by the thick **deltoid muscle**, which forms the rounded superior part of the shoulder. Intramuscular injections are often given into the

deltoid, about 5 cm (2 inches) inferior to the greater tubercle (Figure 17a).

Arm

According to anatomists, the arm runs only from the shoulder to the elbow, and not beyond.

1. In the arm, palpate the humerus along its entire length, especially along its medial and lateral sides.

2. Feel the **biceps brachii** muscle contract on your anterior arm when you flex your forearm against resistance. The medial boundary of the biceps is represented by the **medial bicipital furrow** (Figure 9). This groove contains the large *brachial artery*, and by pressing on it with your fingertips you can feel your *brachial pulse*. The brachial artery is the artery routinely used in measuring blood pressure with a sphygmomanometer.

3. All three heads of the **triceps brachii** muscle (lateral, long, and medial) are visible through the skin of a muscular person (**Figure 10**).

Elbow Region

1. In the distal part of your arm, near the elbow, palpate the two projections of the humerus, the **lateral** and **medial epicondyles** (Figures 9 and 10). Midway between the epicondyles, on the posterior side, feel the **olecranon**, which forms the point of the elbow.

2. Confirm that the two epicondyles and the olecranon all lie in the same horizontal line when the elbow is extended. If these three bony processes do not line up, the elbow is dislocated.

Figure 9 Shoulder and arm.

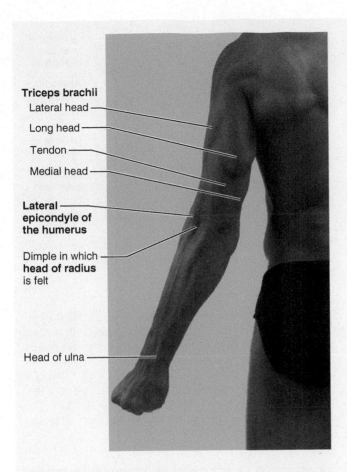

Triceps brachii
  Lateral head
  Long head
  Tendon
  Medial head

Lateral epicondyle of the humerus

Dimple in which **head of radius** is felt

Head of ulna

Figure 10 Surface anatomy of the upper limb, posterior view.

3. Now feel along the posterior surface of the medial epicondyle. You are palpating your ulnar nerve.

4. On the anterior surface of the elbow is a triangular depression called the **cubital fossa (Figure 11)**. The triangle's superior *base* is formed by a horizontal line between the humeral epicondyles; its two inferior sides are defined by the **brachioradialis** and **pronator teres** muscles (Figure 11b). Try to define these boundaries on your own limb. To find the brachioradialis muscle, flex your forearm against resistance, and watch this muscle bulge through the skin of your lateral forearm. To feel your pronator teres contract, palpate the cubital fossa as you pronate your forearm against resistance. (Have your partner provide the resistance.)

Superficially, the cubital fossa contains the **median cubital vein** (Figure 11a). Clinicians often draw blood from this superficial vein and insert intravenous (IV) catheters into it to administer medications, transfused blood, and nutrient fluids. The large **brachial artery** lies just deep to the median cubital vein (Figure 11b), so a needle must be inserted into the vein from a shallow angle (almost parallel to the skin) to avoid puncturing the artery. Tendons and nerves are also found deep in the fossa (Figure 11b).

5. The median cubital vein interconnects the larger **cephalic** and **basilic veins** of the upper limb. These veins are visible through the skin of lean people (Figure 11a). Examine your arm to see if your cephalic and basilic veins are visible.

Forearm and Hand

The two parallel bones of the forearm are the medial *ulna* and the lateral *radius*.

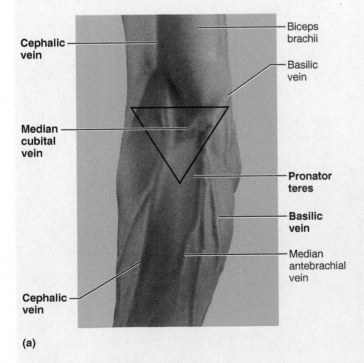

Cephalic vein

Biceps brachii

Basilic vein

Median cubital vein

Pronator teres

Basilic vein

Median antebrachial vein

Cephalic vein

(a)

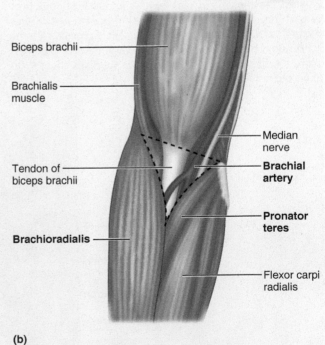

Biceps brachii

Brachialis muscle

Tendon of biceps brachii

Brachioradialis

Median nerve

Brachial artery

Pronator teres

Flexor carpi radialis

(b)

Figure 11 The cubital fossa on the anterior surface of the right elbow (outlined by the triangle). (a) Photograph. **(b)** Diagram of deeper structures in the fossa.

Text continues on next page. →

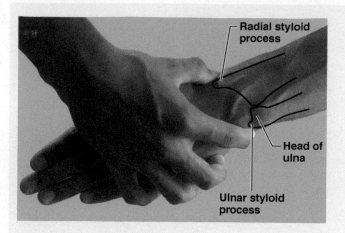

Figure 12 A way to locate the ulnar and radial styloid processes. The right hand is palpating the left hand in this picture. Note that the head of the ulna is not the same as the ulnar styloid process. The radial styloid process lies about 1 cm distal to the ulnar styloid process.

1. Feel the ulna along its entire length as a sharp ridge on the posterior forearm (confirm that this ridge runs inferiorly from the olecranon). As for the radius, you can feel its distal half, but most of its proximal half is covered by muscle. You can, however, feel the rotating **head** of the radius. To do this, extend your forearm, and note that a dimple forms on the posterior lateral surface of the elbow region (Figure 10). Press three fingers into this dimple, and rotate your free hand as if you were turning a doorknob. You will feel the head of the radius rotate as you perform this action.

2. Both the radius and ulna have a knoblike **styloid process** at their distal ends. Palpate these processes at the wrist (**Figure 12**). Do not confuse the ulnar styloid process with the conspicuous **head of the ulna**, from which the styloid process stems. Confirm that the radial styloid process lies about 1 cm (0.4 inch) distal to that of the ulna.

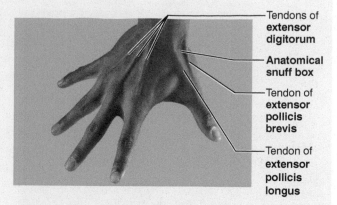

Figure 14 The dorsal surface of the hand. Note especially the anatomical snuff box and dorsal venous network.

Colles' fracture of the wrist is an impacted fracture in which the distal end of the radius is pushed proximally into the shaft of the radius. This sometimes occurs when someone falls on outstretched hands, and it most often happens to elderly women with osteoporosis. Colles' fracture bends the wrist into curves that resemble those on a fork. ✚

Can you deduce how physicians use palpation to diagnose Colles' fracture?

_____

_____

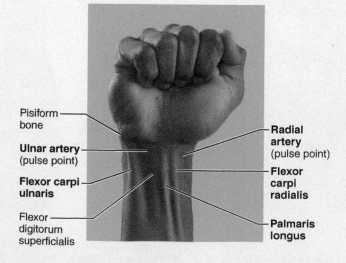

Figure 13 The anterior surface of the distal forearm and fist. The tendons of the flexor muscles guide the clinician to several sites for pulse taking.

3. Next, feel the major groups of muscles within your forearm. Flex your hand and fingers against resistance, and feel the anterior *flexor muscles* contract. Then extend your hand at the wrist, and feel the tightening of the posterior *extensor muscles*.

4. Near the wrist, the anterior surface of the forearm reveals many significant features (**Figure 13**). Flex your fist against resistance; the tendons of the main wrist flexors will bulge the skin of the distal forearm. The tendons of the **flexor carpi radialis** and **palmaris longus** muscles are most obvious. The palmaris longus, however, is absent from at least one arm in 30% of all people, so your forearm may exhibit just one prominent tendon instead of two. The **radial artery** lies just lateral to (on the thumb side of) the flexor carpi radialis tendon, where the pulse is easily detected (Figure 13). Feel your radial pulse here. The *median nerve*, which innervates the thumb, lies deep to the palmaris longus tendon. Finally, the **ulnar artery** lies on the medial side of the forearm, just lateral to the tendon of the **flexor carpi ulnaris**. Locate and feel your ulnar arterial pulse (Figure 13).

5. Extend your thumb and point it posteriorly to form a triangular depression in the base of the thumb on the back of your hand. This is the **anatomical snuff box** (**Figure 14**). Its two elevated borders are defined by the tendons of the thumb extensor muscles, **extensor pollicis brevis** and **extensor pollicis longus**. The radial artery runs within the snuff box, so this is another site for taking a radial pulse. The main bone on the floor of the snuff box is the scaphoid bone of the wrist, but the radial styloid process is also present here. If displaced by a bone fracture, the radial styloid process will be felt outside of the snuff box rather than within it. The "snuff box" took its name from the fact that people once put snuff (tobacco for sniffing) in this hollow before lifting it up to the nose.

6. On the dorsal surface of your hand, observe the superficial veins just deep to the skin. This is the **dorsal venous network**, which drains superiorly into the cephalic vein. This venous network provides a site for drawing blood and inserting intravenous catheters and is preferred over the median cubital vein for these purposes. Next, extend your hand and fingers, and observe the tendons of the **extensor digitorum** muscle.

7. The anterior surface of the hand also contains some features of interest (**Figure 15**). These features include the *epidermal ridges* (fingerprints) and many **flexion creases** in the skin. Grasp your **thenar eminence** (the bulge on the palm that contains the thumb muscles) and your **hypothenar eminence** (the bulge on the medial palm that contains muscles that move the little finger).

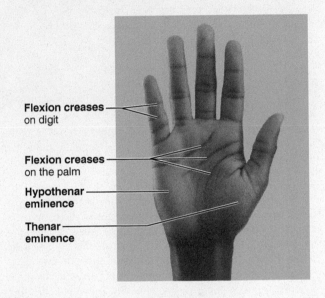

Flexion creases on digit

Flexion creases on the palm

Hypothenar eminence

Thenar eminence

Figure 15 The palmar surface of the hand.

Palpating Landmarks of the Lower Limb

Gluteal Region

Dominating the gluteal region are the two *prominences* (cheeks) of the buttocks (**Figure 16**). These are formed by subcutaneous fat and by the thick **gluteus maximus** muscles. The midline groove between the two prominences is called the **natal cleft** (*natal* = rump) or **gluteal cleft**. The inferior margin of each prominence is the horizontal **gluteal fold**, which roughly corresponds to the inferior margin of the gluteus maximus.

1. Try to palpate your **ischial tuberosity** just above the medial side of each gluteal fold (it will be easier to feel if you sit down or flex your thigh first). The ischial tuberosities are the robust inferior parts of the ischial bones, and they support the body's weight during sitting.

2. Next, palpate the **greater trochanter** of the femur on the lateral side of your hip. This trochanter lies just anterior to a hollow and about 10 cm (one hand's breadth, or 4 inches) inferior to the iliac crest. To confirm that you have found the greater trochanter, alternately flex and extend your thigh. Because this trochanter is the most superior point on the lateral femur, it moves with the femur as you perform this movement.

3. To palpate the sharp **posterior superior iliac spine**, locate your iliac crests again, and trace each to its most posterior point. You may have difficulty feeling this spine, but it is indicated by a distinct dimple in the skin that is easy to find. This dimple lies two to three finger breadths lateral to the midline of the back. The dimple also indicates the position of the *sacroiliac joint*, where the hip bone attaches to the sacrum of the spinal column. You can check *your* "dimples" out in the privacy of your home.

The gluteal region is a major site for administering intramuscular injections. When such injections are given, extreme care must be taken to avoid piercing the major nerve that lies just deep to the gluteus maximus muscle.

This thick *sciatic nerve* innervates much of the lower limb. Furthermore, the needle must avoid the gluteal nerves and gluteal blood vessels, which also lie deep to the gluteus maximus.

Text continues on next page. →

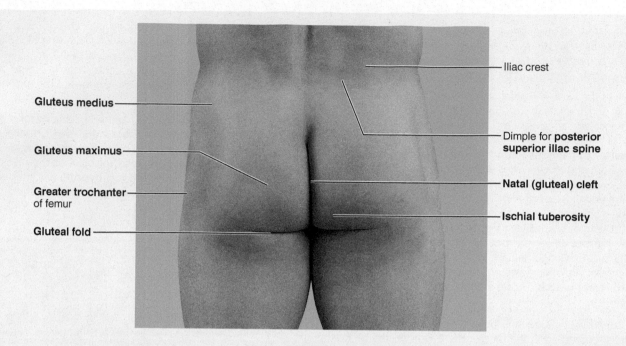

Gluteus medius

Gluteus maximus

Greater trochanter
of femur

Gluteal fold

Iliac crest

Dimple for **posterior
superior iliac spine**

Natal (gluteal) cleft

Ischial tuberosity

Figure 16 The gluteal region. The region extends from the iliac crests superiorly to the gluteal folds inferiorly. Therefore, it includes more than just the prominences of the buttock.

To avoid harming these structures, the injections are most often applied to the **gluteus *medius*** (not maximus) muscle superior to the cheeks of the buttocks, in a safe area called the **ventral gluteal site** (**Figure 17b**). To locate this site, mentally draw a line laterally from the posterior superior iliac spine (dimple) to the greater trochanter; the injection would be given 5 cm (2 inches) superior to the midpoint of that line. Another safe way to locate the ventral gluteal site is to approach the lateral side of the patient's left hip with your extended right hand (or the right hip with your left hand). Then, place your thumb on the anterior superior iliac spine and your index finger as far

posteriorly on the iliac crest as it can reach. The heel of your hand comes to lie on the greater trochanter, and the needle is inserted in the angle of the V formed between your thumb and index finger about 4 cm (1.5 inches) inferior to the iliac crest.

Gluteal injections are not given to small children because their "safe area" is too small to locate with certainty and because the gluteal muscles are thin at this age. Instead, infants and toddlers receive intramuscular shots in the prominent **vastus lateralis** muscle of the thigh (Figure 17c).

Text continues. ➔

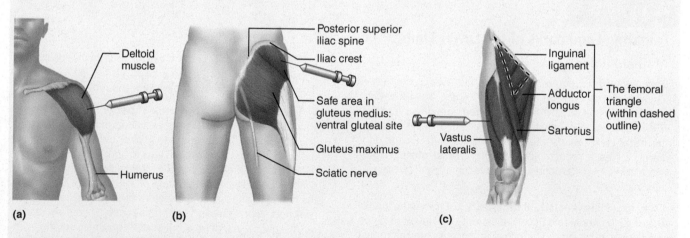

Deltoid
muscle

Humerus

(a)

Posterior superior
iliac spine

Iliac crest

Safe area in
gluteus medius:
ventral gluteal site

Gluteus maximus

Sciatic nerve

(b)

Inguinal
ligament

Adductor
longus

Sartorius

Vastus
lateralis

The femoral
triangle
(within dashed
outline)

(c)

Figure 17 Three major sites of intramuscular injections. (a) Deltoid muscle of the arm (for injection volumes of less than 1 ml). **(b)** Ventral gluteal site (gluteus medius). **(c)** Vastus lateralis in the lateral thigh. The femoral triangle is also shown.

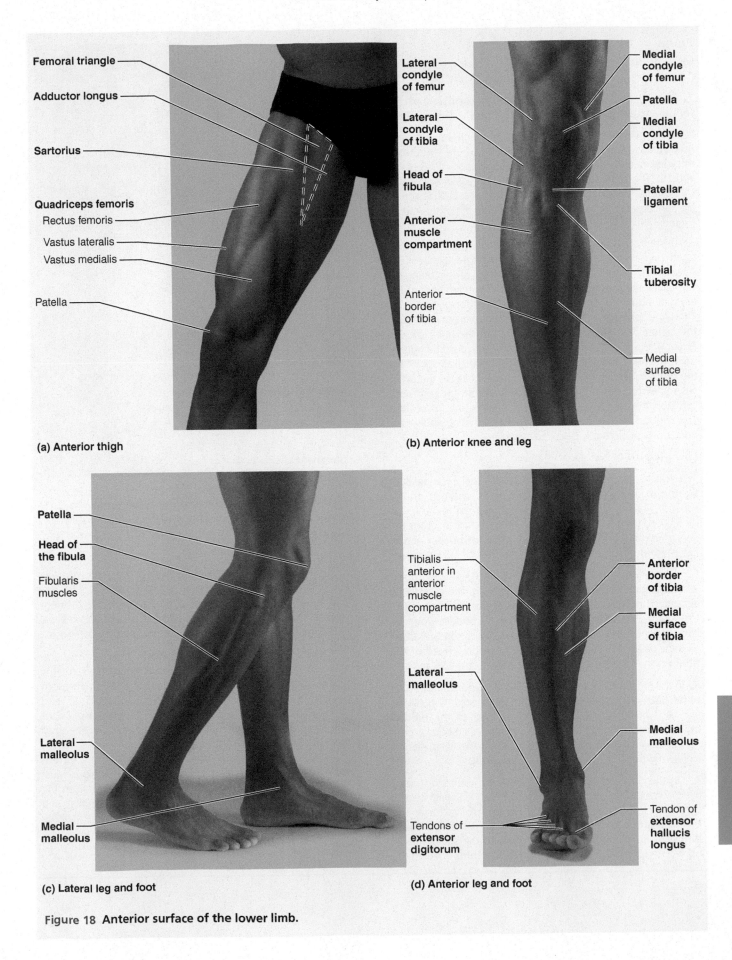

Femoral triangle

Adductor longus

Sartorius

Quadriceps femoris
  Rectus femoris
  Vastus lateralis
  Vastus medialis

Patella

(a) Anterior thigh

Lateral condyle of femur

Lateral condyle of tibia

Head of fibula

Anterior muscle compartment

Anterior border of tibia

Medial condyle of femur

Patella

Medial condyle of tibia

Patellar ligament

Tibial tuberosity

Medial surface of tibia

(b) Anterior knee and leg

Patella

Head of the fibula

Fibularis muscles

Lateral malleolus

Medial malleolus

(c) Lateral leg and foot

Tibialis anterior in anterior muscle compartment

Lateral malleolus

Tendons of extensor digitorum

Anterior border of tibia

Medial surface of tibia

Medial malleolus

Tendon of extensor hallucis longus

(d) Anterior leg and foot

Figure 18 Anterior surface of the lower limb.

23

Thigh

Much of the femur is clothed by thick muscles, so the thigh has few palpable bony landmarks (**Figure 18** and **Figure 19**).

1. Distally, feel the **medial** and **lateral condyles of the femur** and the **patella** anterior to the condyles (Figure 18b).

2. Next, palpate your three groups of thigh muscles—the **quadriceps femoris muscles** anteriorly, the **adductor muscles** medially, and the **hamstrings** posteriorly (Figures 18a and 19). The **vastus lateralis**, the lateral muscle of the quadriceps group, is a site for intramuscular injections. Such injections are administered about halfway down the length of this muscle (Figure 17c).

3. The anterosuperior surface of the thigh exhibits a three-sided depression called the **femoral triangle** (Figure 18a). As shown in Figure 17c, the superior border of this triangle is formed by the **inguinal ligament**, and its two inferior borders are defined by the **sartorius** and **adductor longus** muscles. The large *femoral artery* and *vein* descend vertically through the center of the femoral triangle. To feel the pulse of your femoral artery, press inward just inferior to your midinguinal point (halfway between the anterior superior iliac spine and the pubic tubercle). Be sure to push hard, because the artery lies somewhat deep. By pressing very hard on this point, one can stop the bleeding from a hemorrhage in the lower limb. The femoral triangle also contains most of the *inguinal lymph nodes*, which are easily palpated if swollen.

Leg and Foot

1. Locate your patella again, then follow the thick **patellar ligament** inferiorly from the patella to its insertion on the superior tibia (Figure 18b and c). Here you can feel a rough projection, the **tibial tuberosity**. Continue running your fingers inferiorly along the tibia's sharp **anterior border** and its flat **medial surface**—bony landmarks that lie very near the surface throughout their length.

2. Now, return to the superior part of your leg, and palpate the expanded **lateral** and **medial condyles of the tibia** just inferior to the knee. You can distinguish the tibial condyles from the femoral condyles because you can feel the tibial condyles move with the tibia during knee flexion. Feel the bulbous **head of the fibula** in the superolateral region of the leg (Figure 18b and c).

3. In the most distal part of the leg, feel the **lateral malleolus** of the fibula as the lateral prominence of the ankle (Figure 18c and d). Notice that this lies slightly inferior to the **medial malleolus** of the tibia, which forms the ankle's medial prominence. Place your finger just posterior to the medial malleolus to feel the pulse of your *posterior tibial artery*.

4. On the posterior aspect of the knee is a diamond-shaped hollow called the **popliteal fossa** (Figure 19). Palpate the large muscles that define the four borders of this fossa: The **biceps femoris** forming the superolateral border, the **semitendinosus** and **semimembranosus** defining the superomedial border, and the two heads of the **gastrocnemius** forming the

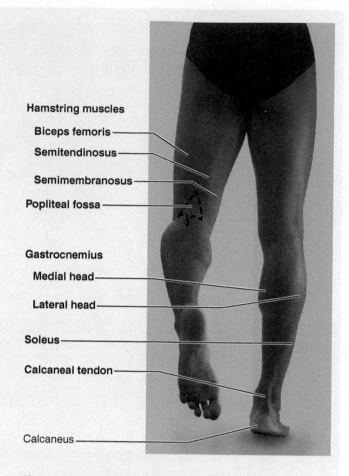

Hamstring muscles
Biceps femoris
Semitendinosus
Semimembranosus
Popliteal fossa

Gastrocnemius
Medial head
Lateral head

Soleus

Calcaneal tendon

Calcaneus

Figure 19 Posterior surface of the lower limb.
Notice the diamond-shaped popliteal fossa posterior to the knee.

inferior border. The main vessels to the leg, the *popliteal artery* and *vein*, lie deep within this fossa. To feel a popliteal pulse, flex your leg at the knee and push your fingers firmly into the popliteal fossa. If a physician is unable to feel a patient's popliteal pulse, the femoral artery may be narrowed by atherosclerosis.

5. Observe the dorsum (superior surface) of your foot. You may see the superficial **dorsal venous arch** overlying the proximal part of the metatarsal bones (Figure 18d). This arch gives rise to both saphenous veins (the main superficial veins of the lower limb). Visible in lean people, the *great saphenous vein* ascends along the medial side of the entire limb. The *small saphenous vein* ascends through the center of the calf.

As you extend your toes, observe the tendons of the **extensor digitorum longus** and **extensor hallucis longus** muscles on the dorsum of the foot. Finally, place a finger on the extreme proximal part of the space between the first and second metatarsal bones. Here you should be able to feel the pulse of the **dorsalis pedis artery**.

REVIEW SHEET

Surface Anatomy Roundup

Name _____ Lab Time/Date _____

_____ 1. A blow to the cheek is most likely to break what superficial bone or bone part? (a) superciliary arches, (b) mastoid process, (c) zygomatic arch, (d) ramus of the mandible

_____ 2. Rebound tenderness (a) occurs in appendicitis, (b) is whiplash of the neck, (c) is a sore foot from playing basketball, (d) occurs when the larynx falls back into place after swallowing.

_____ 3. The anatomical snuff box (a) is in the nose, (b) contains the radial styloid process, (c) is defined by tendons of the flexor carpi radialis and palmaris longus, (d) cannot really hold snuff.

_____ 4. Some landmarks on the body surface can be seen or felt, but others are abstractions that you must construct by drawing imaginary lines. Which of the following pairs of structures is abstract and invisible? (a) umbilicus and costal margin, (b) anterior superior iliac spine and natal cleft, (c) linea alba and linea semilunaris, (d) McBurney's point and midaxillary line, (e) lacrimal fossa and sternocleidomastoid

_____ 5. Many pelvic organs can be palpated by placing a finger in the rectum or the vagina, but only one pelvic organ is readily palpated through the skin. This is the (a) nonpregnant uterus, (b) prostate, (c) full bladder, (d) ovaries, (e) rectum.

_____ 6. Contributing to the posterior axillary fold is/are (a) pectoralis major, (b) latissimus dorsi, (c) trapezius, (d) infraspinatus, (e) pectoralis minor, (f) a and e.

_____ 7. Which of the following is *not* a pulse point? (a) anatomical snuff box, (b) inferior margin of mandible anterior to masseter muscle, (c) center of distal forearm at palmaris longus tendon, (d) medial bicipital furrow on arm, (e) dorsum of foot between the first two metatarsals

_____ 8. Which pair of ribs inserts on the sternum at the sternal angle? (a) first, (b) second, (c) third, (d) fourth, (e) fifth

_____ 9. The inferior angle of the scapula is at the same level as the spinous process of which vertebra? (a) C_5, (b) C_7, (c) T_3, (d) T_7, (e) L_4

_____ 10. An important bony landmark that can be recognized by a distinct dimple in the skin is the (a) posterior superior iliac spine, (b) ulnar styloid process, (c) shaft of the radius, (d) acromion.

_____ 11. A nurse missed a patient's median cubital vein while trying to withdraw blood and then inserted the needle far too deeply into the cubital fossa. This error could cause any of the following problems, *except* this one: (a) paralysis of the ulnar nerve, (b) paralysis of the median nerve, (c) bruising the insertion tendon of the biceps brachii muscle, (d) blood spurting from the brachial artery.

_____ 12. Which of these organs is almost impossible to study with surface anatomy techniques? (a) heart, (b) lungs, (c) brain, (d) nose

_____ 13. A preferred site for inserting an intravenous medication line into a blood vessel is the (a) medial bicipital furrow on arm, (b) external carotid artery, (c) dorsal venous network of hand, (d) popliteal fossa.

_____ 14. One listens for bowel sounds with a stethoscope placed (a) on the four quadrants of the abdominal wall; (b) in the triangle of auscultation; (c) in the right and left midaxillary line, just superior to the iliac crests; (d) inside the patient's bowels (intestines), on the tip of an endoscope.

_____ 15. A stab wound in the posterior triangle of the neck could damage any of the following structures *except* the (a) accessory nerve, (b) phrenic nerve, (c) external jugular vein, (d) external carotid artery.

16. ✚ What procedure requires locating the supracristal line? _____

_____

What disease is this procedure used to detect? _____

17. ✚ Describe the procedure used to detect a full urinary bladder. _____

_____

18. ✚ A patient is experiencing mastoiditis. Where would you expect the inflammation to be located? _____

_____

Credits

Credits are listed in order of appearance.

Photographs

1–3, 5, 7, 9–11a, 12–16, 18, 19: John Wilson White/Pearson Education, Inc.

Dissection and Identification of Cat Muscles

Learning Outcomes

▶ Name and locate muscles on a dissected cat.

▶ Recognize similarities and differences between human and cat musculature.

Materials

▶ Disposable gloves or protective skin cream

▶ Safety glasses

▶ Preserved and injected cat (one for every two to four students)

▶ Dissecting instruments and tray

▶ Name tag and large plastic bag

▶ Paper towels

▶ Embalming fluid

▶ Organic debris container

The skeletal muscles of all mammals are named in a similar fashion. However, some muscles that are separate in lower animals are fused in humans, and some muscles present in lower animals are absent in humans. Dissection of cat musculature, in conjunction with the study of human muscles, will enhance your knowledge of the human muscular system. Since the aim is to become familiar with the muscles of the human body, you should pay particular attention to the similarities between cat and human muscles. However, pertinent differences will be pointed out as you encounter them. Refer to a discussion of the anatomy of the human muscular system as you work.

When dissecting, wear safety glasses and a lab coat or apron over your clothes to prevent staining your clothes with embalming fluid.

Go to Mastering A&P™ > **Study Area to improve your performance in A&P Lab.**

> Animations & Videos > Cat Dissection Videos > Superficial Muscles of the Trunk

Instructors may assign Cat Dissection Videos, Practice Anatomy Lab Practical questions (PAL) for the dissections, and more using the Mastering A&P™ Item Library.

Dissection and Identification of Cat Muscles
ACTIVITY Preparing the Cat for Dissection

Preparing the Cat for Dissection

The preserved laboratory animals purchased for dissection have been embalmed with a solution that prevents deterioration of the tissues. The animals are generally delivered in plastic bags that contain a small amount of the embalming fluid. _Do not dispose of this fluid_ when you remove the cat; the fluid prevents the cat from drying out. It is very important to keep the cat's tissues moist because you will probably use the same cat from now until the end of the course.

1. Don disposable gloves and safety glasses, and then obtain a cat, dissecting tray, dissecting instruments, and a name tag. Using a pencil, mark the name tag with the names of the members of your group, and set it aside. You will attach the name tag to the plastic bag at the end of the dissection so that you can identify your animal in subsequent laboratory sessions.

2. To begin removing the skin, place the cat ventral side down on the dissecting tray. Cutting away from yourself with a newly bladed scalpel, make a short, shallow incision in the midline of the neck, just to penetrate the skin. From this point on, use scissors. Continue to cut the length of the back to the sacro-lumbar region, stopping at the tail (see **Incisions to be made in skinning a cat** figure).

3. From the dorsal surface of the tail region, continue the incision around the tail, encircling the anus and genital organs. The skin will not be removed from this region.

4. Before you begin to remove the skin, check with your instructor. He or she may want you to skin only the right or left side of the cat. Beginning again at the dorsal tail region, make an incision through the skin down each hind leg to be skinned nearly to the ankle. Continue the cut completely around the ankle.

5. Return to the neck. Cut the skin around the circumference of the neck.

6. Cut down each foreleg to be skinned to the wrist. Completely cut through the skin around the wrist (see **Incisions . . .** figure).

7. Now free the skin from the loose connective tissue (superficial fascia) that binds it to the underlying structures. With one hand, grasp the skin on one side of the midline dorsal incision. Then, using your fingers or a blunt probe, break through the "cottony" connective tissue fibers to release the skin from the muscle beneath. Work toward the ventral surface and then toward the neck. As you pull the skin from the body, you should see small, white, cordlike structures extending from the skin to the muscles at fairly regular intervals. These are the cutaneous nerves that serve the skin. You will also see (particularly as you approach the ventral surface) that a thin layer of muscle fibers remains adhered to the skin. This is the **cutaneous maximus** muscle, which enables the cat to move its skin rather like our facial muscles allow us to express emotion. Where the cutaneous maximus fibers cling to those of the deeper muscles, carefully cut them free. Along the ventral surface of the trunk, notice the two lines of nipples associated with the mammary glands. These are more prominent in females, especially if they are pregnant or were recently lactating.

8. You will notice as you start to free the skin in the neck that it is more difficult to remove. Take extra care and time in this area. The large flat **platysma** muscle in the ventral neck region (a skin muscle like the cutaneous maximus) will remain attached to the skin. The skin will not be removed from the top of the head since the cat's head muscles are not sufficiently similar to human head muscles to merit study.

9. Complete the skinning process by freeing the skin from the forelimbs, the lower torso, and the hindlimbs in the same manner. The skin may be more difficult to remove as you approach the paws so you may need to take additional time in these areas to avoid damaging the underlying muscles and tendons. _Do not discard the skin._

10. Inspect your skinned cat. Notice that it is difficult to see any cleavage lines between the muscles because of the overlying connective tissue, which is white or yellow. If time allows, carefully remove as much of the fat and fascia from the surface of the muscles as possible, using forceps or your fingers. The muscles, when exposed, look grainy or threadlike and are light brown. If you carry out this clearing process carefully and thoroughly, you will be ready to begin your identification of the superficial muscles.

11. If muscle dissection exercises are to be done at a later laboratory session, follow the cleanup instructions noted in the box below. _Prepare your cat for storage in this way every time the cat is used._

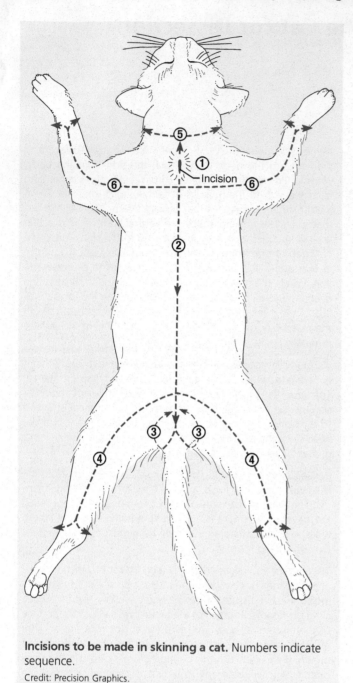

Incisions to be made in skinning a cat. Numbers indicate sequence.

Credit: Precision Graphics.

Preparing the Dissection Animal for Storage

1. To prevent the internal organs from drying out, dampen a layer of folded paper towels with embalming fluid, and wrap them snugly around the animal's torso. (Do not use *water-soaked* paper towels, which encourages mold growth.) Make sure the dissected areas are completely enveloped.

2. Return the animal's skin flaps to their normal position over the ventral cavity body organs.

3. Place the animal in a plastic storage bag. Add more embalming fluid if necessary, press out excess air, and securely close the bag with a rubber band or twine.

4. Make sure your name tag is securely attached, and place the animal in the designated storage container.

5. Clean all dissecting equipment with soapy water, rinse, and dry it for return to the storage area. Wash down the lab bench, and properly dispose of organic debris and your gloves before leaving the laboratory. Return safety glasses to the appropriate location.

Activity

Dissecting Neck and Trunk Muscles

The proper dissection of muscles involves careful separation of one muscle from another and transection of superficial muscles in order to study those lying deeper. In general, when you are instructed to **transect** a muscle, you should first completely free it from all adhering connective tissue and *then* cut through the belly (fleshiest part) of the muscle about halfway between its origin and insertion points. *Use caution when working around points of muscle origin or insertion, and do not remove the fascia associated with such attachments.*

As a rule, all the fibers of one muscle are held together by a connective tissue sheath (epimysium) and run in the same general direction. Before you begin dissection, observe your skinned cat. If you look carefully, you can see changes in the direction of the muscle fibers, which will help you to locate the muscle borders. Pulling in slightly different directions on two adjacent muscles will usually expose subtle white lines created by the connective tissue surrounding the muscles and allow you to find the normal cleavage line between them. After you

have identified cleavage lines, *use a blunt probe* to break the connective tissue between muscles and to separate them. If the muscles separate as clean, distinct bundles, your procedure is probably correct. If they appear ragged or chewed up, you are probably tearing a muscle apart rather than separating it from adjacent muscles. Because of time considerations, in this exercise you will identify only the muscles that are most easily identified and separated out.

Anterior Neck Muscles

1. Examine the anterior neck surface of the cat, and identify the following superficial neck muscles. The *platysma* belongs in this group but was probably removed during the skinning process. Refer to the figure **Superficial muscles of the anterior neck of the cat** as you work. The **sternomastoid** muscle and the more lateral and deeper **cleidomastoid** muscle (not visible in the **figure**), are joined in humans to form the sterno-cleidomastoid. The large external jugular veins, which drain the

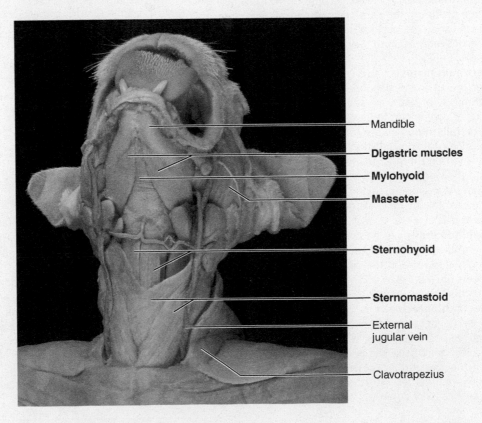

— Mandible
— **Digastric muscles**
— **Mylohyoid**
— **Masseter**
— **Sternohyoid**
— **Sternomastoid**
— External jugular vein
— Clavotrapezius

Superficial muscles of the anterior neck of the cat.

Credits: Illustration: Imagineering STA Media Services; photo: Shawn Miller (dissection) and Mark Nielsen (photography), Pearson Education.

head, should be obvious crossing the anterior aspect of these muscles. The **mylohyoid** muscle parallels the bottom aspect of the chin, and the **digastric** muscles form a V over the mylohyoid muscle. Although it is not one of the neck muscles, you can now identify the fleshy **masseter** muscle, which flanks the digastric muscle laterally. Finally, the **sternohyoid** is a narrow muscle between the mylohyoid (superiorly) and the inferior sternomastoid.

2. The deeper muscles of the anterior neck of the cat are small and straplike and hardly worth the effort of dissection. However, one of these deeper muscles can be seen with a minimum of extra effort. Transect the sternomastoid and sternohyoid muscles approximately at midbelly. Reflect the cut ends to reveal the bandlike **sternothyroid** muscle (not visible in the **figure**), which runs along the anterior surface of the throat just deep and lateral to the sternohyoid muscle. The cleidomastoid muscle, which lies deep to the sternomastoid, is also more easily identified now.

Superficial Chest Muscles

In the cat, the chest or pectoral muscles adduct the arm, just as they do in humans. However, humans have only two pectoral muscles, and cats have four—the pectoralis major, pectoralis minor, xiphihumeralis, and pectoantebrachialis (see the figure **Superficial muscles of the thorax and abdominal wall, ventral view**). However, because of their relatively great degree of fusion, the cat's pectoral muscles appear to be a single muscle. The pectoral muscles are rather difficult to dissect and identify because they do not separate from one another easily.

The **pectoralis major** is 5 to 8 cm (2 to 3 inches) wide and can be seen arising on the manubrium, just inferior to the sternomastoid muscle of the neck, and running to the humerus. Its fibers run at right angles to the long axis of the cat's body.

The **pectoralis minor** lies beneath the pectoralis major and extends posterior to it on the abdominal surface. It originates on the sternum and inserts on the humerus. Its fibers run obliquely to the long axis of the body, which helps to distinguish it from the pectoralis major. Contrary to what its name implies, the pectoralis minor is a larger and thicker muscle than the pectoralis major.

The **xiphihumeralis** can be distinguished from the posterior edge of the pectoralis minor only by virtue of the fact that its origin is lower—on the xiphoid process of the sternum. Its fibers run parallel to and are fused with those of the pectoralis minor.

The **pectoantebrachialis** is a thin, straplike muscle, about 1.3 cm (½ inch) wide, lying over the pectoralis major. Notice that the pectoralis major is visible both anterior and posterior to the borders of the pectoantebrachialis. It originates from the manubrium, passes laterally over the pectoralis major, and merges with the muscles of the forelimb approximately halfway down the humerus. It has no homologue in humans.

Identify, free, and trace out the origin and insertion of the cat's chest muscles (refer to **Superficial muscles of the thorax and abdominal wall . . .** figure).

Muscles of the Abdominal Wall

The superficial trunk muscles include those of the abdominal wall (see the figures **Superficial muscles of the thorax and**

abdominal wall . . . and **Muscles of the abdominal wall of the cat**. Cat musculature in this area is quite similar in function to that of humans.

1. Complete the dissection of the more superficial anterior trunk muscles of the cat by identifying the origins and insertions of the muscles of the abdominal wall. Work carefully here. These muscles are very thin, and it is easy to miss their boundaries. Begin with the **rectus abdominis**, a long band of muscle approximately 2.5 cm (1 inch) wide running immediately lateral to the midline of the body on the abdominal surface. Humans have four transverse *tendinous intersections* in the rectus abdominis, but they are absent or difficult to identify in the cat. Identify the **linea alba**, the longitudinal band of connective tissue that separates the rectus abdominis muscles. Note the relationship of the rectus abdominis to the other abdominal muscles and their fascia.

2. The **external oblique** is a sheet of muscle immediately beside the rectus abdominis (see **Muscles of the abdominal wall . . .** figure). Carefully free and then transect the external oblique to reveal the anterior attachment of the rectus abdominis. Reflect the external oblique; observe the deeper **internal oblique** muscle. Notice which way the fibers run.

How does the fiber direction of the internal oblique compare to that of the external oblique?

_____

_____

3. Free and then transect the internal oblique muscle to reveal the fibers of the **transversus abdominis**, whose fibers run transversely across the abdomen.

Superficial Muscles of the Shoulder and the Dorsal Trunk and Neck

Dissect the superficial muscles of the dorsal surface of the trunk. Refer to the figure **Superficial muscles of the anterodorsal aspect of the shoulder, trunk, and neck of the cat**.

1. Turn your cat on its ventral surface, and start your observations with the **trapezius group**. Humans have a single large *trapezius muscle*, but the cat has three separate muscles—the clavotrapezius, acromiotrapezius, and spinotrapezius—that together perform a similar function. The prefix in each case (clavo-, acromio-, and spino-) reveals the muscle's site of insertion. The **clavotrapezius**, the most anterior muscle of the group, is homologous to that part of the human trapezius that inserts into the clavicle. Slip a probe under this muscle, and follow it to its apparent origin.

Where does the clavotrapezius appear to originate?

_____

Is this similar to its origin in humans? _____

The fibers of the clavotrapezius are continuous posteriorly with those of the clavicular part of the cat's deltoid muscle (clavodeltoid), and the two muscles work together to flex the humerus. Release the clavotrapezius muscle from adjoining

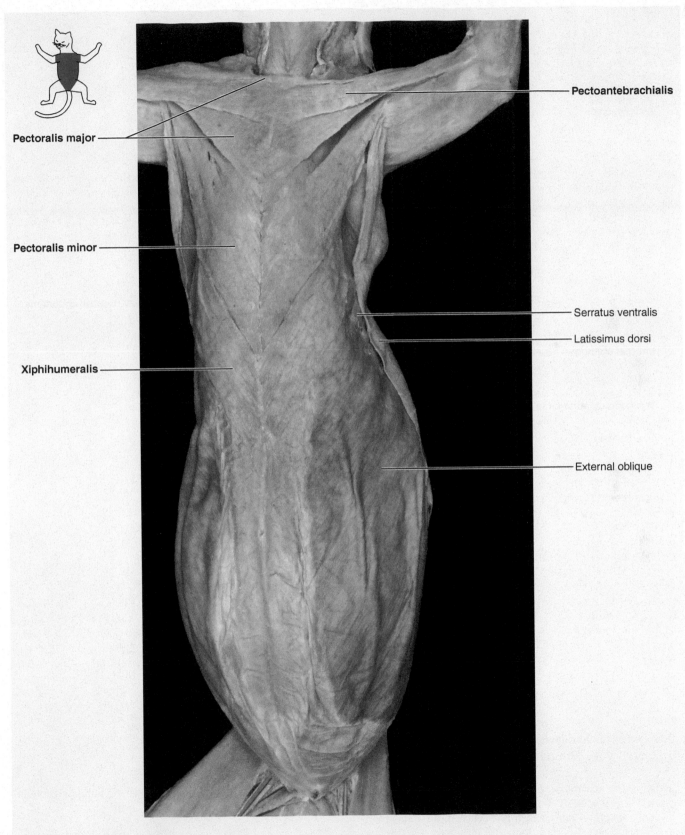

Pectoantebrachialis

Pectoralis major

Pectoralis minor

Serratus ventralis

Latissimus dorsi

Xiphihumeralis

External oblique

Superficial muscles of the thorax and abdominal wall, ventral view.
Note location of the latissimus dorsi.

Credits: Illustration: Imagineering STA Media Services; photo: Shawn Miller (dissection) and Mark Nielsen (photography), Pearson Education.

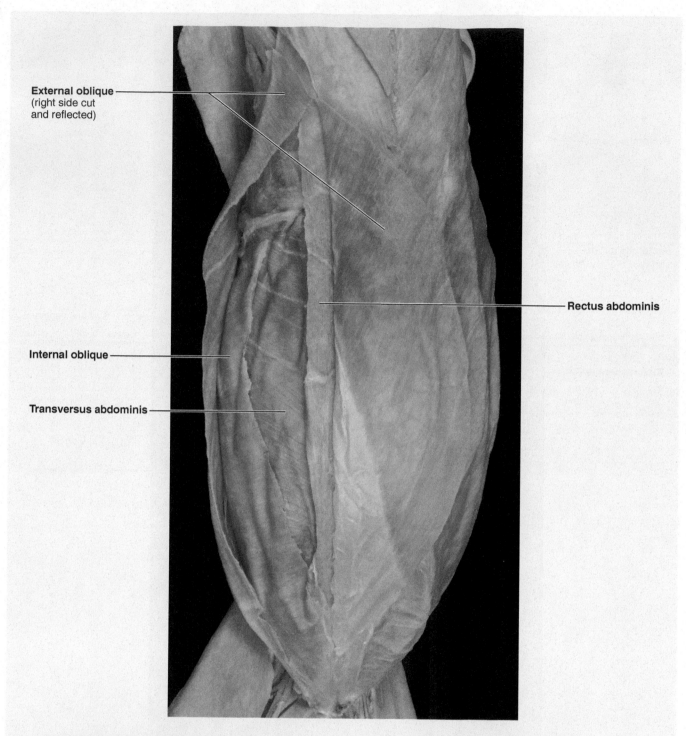

Muscles of the abdominal wall of the cat.

Photo credits: Shawn Miller (dissection) and Mark Nielsen (photography), Pearson Education.

muscles. The **acromiotrapezius** is a large, thin, nearly square muscle easily identified by its aponeurosis, which passes over the vertebral border of the scapula. It originates from the cervical and T$_1$ vertebrae and inserts into the scapular spine. The triangular **spinotrapezius** runs from the thoracic vertebrae to the scapular spine. This is the most posterior of the trapezius muscles in the cat. Now that you know where they are located, pull on the three trapezius muscles to mimic their action.

Do the trapezius muscles appear to have the same functions in cats as in humans?

2. The **levator scapulae ventralis**, a flat, straplike muscle, can be located in the triangle created by the division of the fibers of the clavotrapezius and acromiotrapezius. Its anterior fibers run underneath the clavotrapezius from its origin at the occipital bone, and it inserts on the vertebral border of

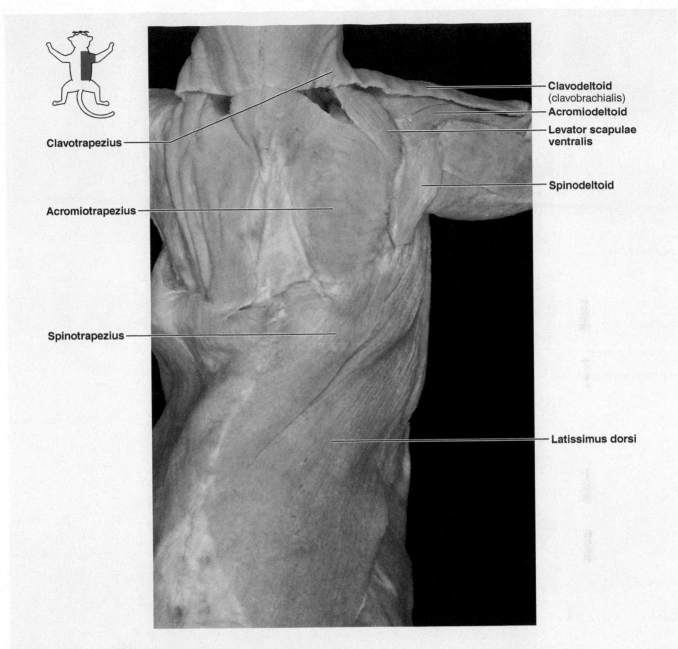

Clavotrapezius

Acromiotrapezius

Spinotrapezius

Clavodeltoid (clavobrachialis)
Acromiodeltoid
Levator scapulae ventralis

Spinodeltoid

Latissimus dorsi

Superficial muscles of the anterodorsal aspect of the shoulder, trunk, and neck of the cat.

Credits: Illustration: Imagineering STA Media Services; photo: Shawn Miller (dissection) and Mark Nielsen (photography), Pearson Education.

the scapula. In the cat it helps to hold the upper edges of the scapulae together and draws them toward the head.

What is the function of the levator scapulae in humans?

_____

_____

3. The **deltoid group**: Like the trapezius, the human *deltoid muscle* is represented by three separate muscles in the cat—the clavodeltoid, acromiodeltoid, and spinodeltoid. The **clavodeltoid** (also called the *clavobrachialis*), the most superficial muscle of the shoulder, is a continuation of the clavotrapezius below the

clavicle, which is this muscle's point of origin (see the **Superficial muscles of the anterodorsal aspect of the shoulder, trunk, and neck . . .** figure). Follow its path down the forelimb to the point where it merges along a white line with the pectoantebrachialis. Separate it from the pectoantebrachialis, and then transect it and pull it back.

Where does the clavodeltoid insert? _____

What do you think the function of this muscle is?

_____

_____

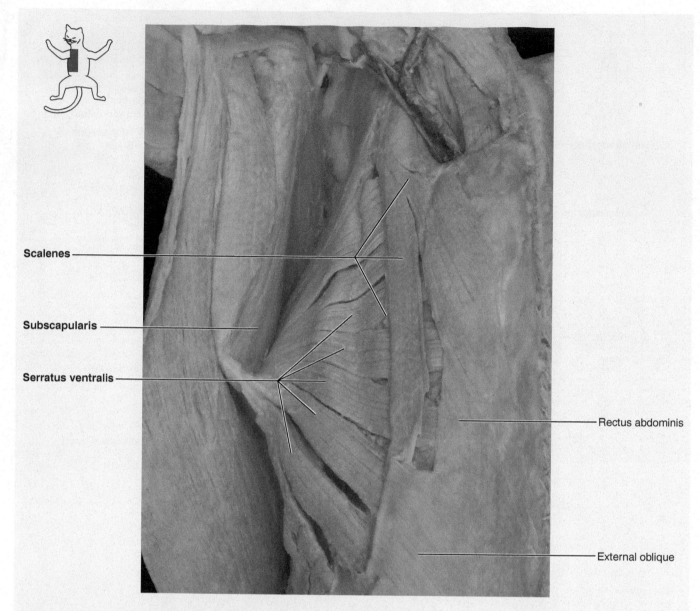

Scalenes

Subscapularis

Serratus ventralis

Rectus abdominis

External oblique

Deep muscles of the inferolateral thorax of the cat.

Credits: Illustration: Imagineering STA Media Services; photo: Shawn Miller (dissection) and Mark Nielsen (photography), Pearson Education.

The **acromiodeltoid** lies posterior to the clavodeltoid and runs over the top of the shoulder. This small triangular muscle originates on the acromion of the scapula. It inserts into the spinodeltoid (a muscle of similar size) posterior to it. The **spinodeltoid** is covered with fascia near the anterior end of the scapula. Its tendon extends under the acromiodeltoid muscle and inserts on the humerus. Notice that its fibers run obliquely to those of the acromiodeltoid. Like the human deltoid muscle, the acromiodeltoid and spinodeltoid muscles in the cat abduct and rotate the humerus.

4. The **latissimus dorsi** is a large, thick, flat muscle covering most of the lateral surface of the posterior trunk; it extends and adducts the arm. Its anterior edge is covered by the spinotrapezius and may appear ragged because it has been cut off from the cutaneous maximus muscle attached to the skin. As in humans, it inserts into the humerus. But before dissecting, its fibers merge with the fibers of many other muscles, among them the xiphihumeralis of the pectoralis group.

Deep Muscles of the Laterodorsal Trunk and Neck

1. In preparation for identifying deep muscles of the dorsal trunk, transect the latissimus dorsi, the muscles of the pectoralis group, and the spinotrapezius and reflect them back. Be careful not to damage the large brachial nerve plexus, which lies in the axillary space beneath the pectoralis group.

2. The **serratus ventralis** corresponds to two separate muscles in humans. The posterior portion is homologous to the *serratus anterior* of humans, arising deep to the pectoral muscles and covering the lateral surface of the rib cage. It is easily identified by its fingerlike muscular origins, which arise on the first 9 or 10 ribs. It inserts into the scapula (see the figure **Deep muscles of the inferolateral thorax of the cat**). The anterior portion of the serratus ventralis, which arises from the cervical vertebrae, is homologous to the *levator scapulae* in humans; both pull the scapula toward the sternum. Trace this muscle to its insertion. In general, in the cat, this muscle pulls the scapula posteriorly and downward.

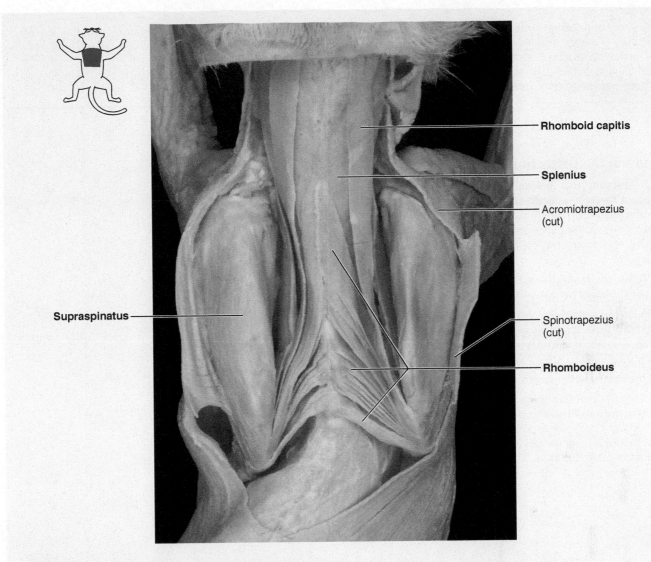

Rhomboid capitis

Splenius

Acromiotrapezius
(cut)

Supraspinatus

Spinotrapezius
(cut)

Rhomboideus

Deep muscles of the superior aspect of the dorsal thorax of the cat.

Credits: Illustration: Imagineering STA Media Services; photo: Shawn Miller (dissection) and Mark Nielsen
(photography), Pearson Education.

3. Reflect the upper limb to reveal the **subscapularis**, which occupies most of the ventral surface of the scapula (see **Deep muscles of the inferolateral thorax . . .** figure). Humans have a homologous muscle.

4. Locate the anterior, posterior, and middle **scalene** muscles on the lateral surface of the cat's neck and trunk. The most prominent and longest of these muscles is the middle scalene, which lies between the anterior and posterior members. The scalenes originate on the ribs and run cephalad over the serratus ventralis to insert in common on the cervical vertebrae. These muscles draw the ribs anteriorly and bend the neck downward; thus they are homologous to the human scalene muscles, which elevate the ribs and flex the neck. (Notice that the difference is only one of position. Humans walk erect, but cats are quadrupeds.)

5. Reflect the flaps of the transected latissimus dorsi, spinodeltoid, acromiodeltoid, and levator scapulae ventralis. The **splenius** is a large flat muscle occupying most of the side of the neck close to the vertebrae (see the figure **Deep muscles of**

the superior aspect of the dorsal thorax of the cat). As in humans, it originates on the ligamentum nuchae at the back of the neck and inserts into the occipital bone. It raises the head.

6. To view the rhomboid muscles, lay the cat on its side and hold its forelegs together to spread the scapulae apart. The rhomboid muscles lie between the scapulae and beneath the acromiotrapezius. All the rhomboid muscles originate on the vertebrae and insert on the scapula. They hold the dorsal part of the scapula to the cat's back.

There are three rhomboids in the cat. The ribbonlike **rhomboid capitis**, the most anterolateral muscle of the group, has no counterpart in the human body. The **rhomboid minor**, located posterior to the rhomboid capitis, is much larger. The fibers of the rhomboid minor run transversely to those of the rhomboid capitis. The most posterior muscle of the group, the **rhomboid major**, is so closely fused to the rhomboid minor that many consider them to be one muscle—the **rhomboideus**, which is homologous to human *rhomboid muscles.*

7. The **supraspinatus** and **infraspinatus** muscles are similar to the same muscles in humans. The supraspinatus can be found under the acromiotrapezius, and the infraspinatus is deep to the spinotrapezius. Both originate on the lateral scapular surface and insert on the humerus.

8. If this activity concludes your laboratory session, follow the cleanup instructions in the accompanying box.

Preparing the Dissection Animal for Storage

1. To prevent the internal organs from drying out, dampen a layer of folded paper towels with embalming fluid, and wrap them snugly around the animal's torso. (Do not use *water-soaked* paper towels, which encourages mold growth.) Make sure the dissected areas are completely enveloped.

2. Return the animal's skin flaps to their normal position over the ventral cavity body organs.

3. Place the animal in a plastic storage bag. Add more embalming fluid if necessary, press out excess air, and securely close the bag with a rubber band or twine.

4. Make sure your name tag is securely attached, and place the animal in the designated storage container.

5. Clean all dissecting equipment with soapy water, rinse, and dry it for return to the storage area. Wash down the lab bench, and properly dispose of organic debris and your gloves before leaving the laboratory. Return safety glasses to the appropriate location.

Dissection and Identification of Cat Muscles
ACTIVITY Dissecting Forelimb Muscles

Activity

Dissecting Forelimb Muscles

Cat forelimb muscles fall into the same three categories as human upper limb muscles, but in this section the muscles of the entire forelimb are considered together (refer to the figure **Lateral surface of the forelimb of the cat**).

Muscles of the Lateral Surface

1. The **triceps brachii** muscle of the cat is easily identified if the cat is placed on its side. It is a large fleshy muscle covering the posterior aspect and much of the side of the humerus. As in humans, this muscle arises from three heads, which originate from the humerus and scapula and insert jointly into the olecranon of the ulna. Remove the fascia from the superior region of the lateral arm surface to identify the lateral and long heads of the triceps. The long head is approximately twice as long as the lateral head and lies medial to it on the posterior arm surface. The medial head can be exposed by transecting the lateral head and pulling it aside. Now pull on the triceps muscle.

How does the function of the triceps muscle compare in cats and in humans?

Anterior and distal to the medial head of the triceps is the tiny **anconeus** muscle (not visible in **figure**), sometimes called the fourth head of the triceps muscle. Notice its darker color and the way it wraps the tip of the elbow.

2. The **brachialis** can be located anterior to the lateral head of the triceps muscle. Identify its origin on the humerus, and trace its course as it crosses the elbow and inserts on the ulna. It flexes the cat's foreleg.

Identifying the forearm muscles is difficult because of the tough fascia sheath that encases them, but give it a try.

3. Remove as much of the connective tissue as possible, and cut through the ligaments that secure the tendons at the wrist (transverse carpal ligaments) so that you will be able to follow the muscles to their insertions. Begin your identification of the forearm muscles at the lateral surface of the forearm. The muscles of this region look very similar and are difficult to identify accurately unless a definite order is followed. Thus you will begin with the most anterior muscles and proceed to the posterior aspect. Remember to check carefully the tendons of insertion to verify your muscle identifications.

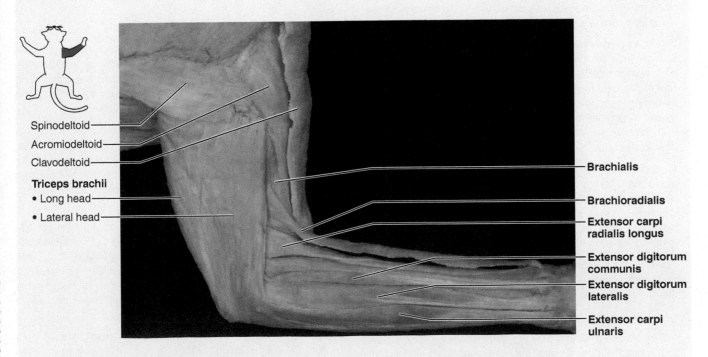

Spinodeltoid
Acromiodeltoid
Clavodeltoid

Triceps brachii
• Long head
• Lateral head

Brachialis
Brachioradialis
Extensor carpi radialis longus
Extensor digitorum communis
Extensor digitorum lateralis
Extensor carpi ulnaris

Lateral surface of the forelimb of the cat.

Credits: Illustration: Imagineering STA Media Services; photo: Shawn Miller (dissection) and Mark Nielsen (photography), Pearson Education.

From Dissection Exercise 1, Activity 3, of *Human Anatomy & Physiology Laboratory Manual, Cat Version* Thirteenth Edition. Elaine N. Marieb and Lori Smith. Copyright © 2019 by Pearson Education, Inc. All rights reserved.

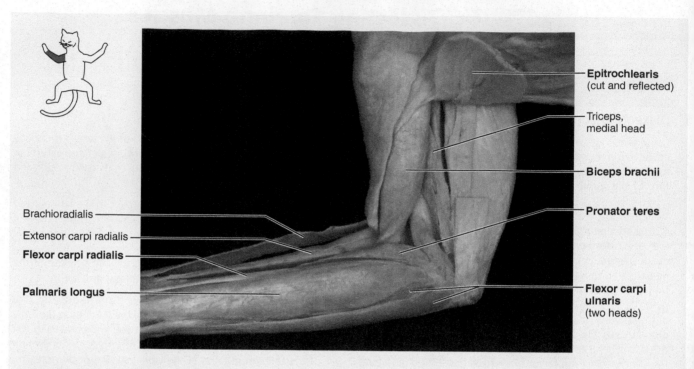

Epitrochlearis
(cut and reflected)

Triceps,
medial head

Biceps brachii

Pronator teres

Brachioradialis

Extensor carpi radialis

Flexor carpi radialis

Palmaris longus

**Flexor carpi
ulnaris**
(two heads)

Medial surface of the forelimb of the cat.

Credits: Illustration: Imagineering STA Media Services; photo: Shawn Miller (dissection) and Mark Nielsen
(photography), Pearson Education.

4. The ribbonlike muscle on the lateral surface of the humerus is the **brachioradialis**. Observe how it passes down the forearm to insert on the radial styloid process. (If you did not remove the fascia very carefully, you may have also removed this muscle.)

5. The **extensor carpi radialis longus** has a broad origin and is larger than the brachioradialis. It extends down the anterior surface of the radius (see **Lateral surface of the forelimb . . .** figure). Transect this muscle to view the **extensor carpi radialis brevis** (not shown in the **figure**), which is partially covered by and sometimes fused with the extensor carpi radialis longus. Both muscles have origins, insertions, and actions similar to their human counterparts.

6. You can see the entire **extensor digitorum communis** along the lateral surface of the forearm. Trace it to its four tendons, which insert on the second to fifth digits. This muscle extends these digits. The **extensor digitorum lateralis** (absent in humans) also extends the digits. This muscle lies immediately posterior to the extensor digitorum communis.

7. Follow the **extensor carpi ulnaris** from the lateral epicondyle of the humerus to the ulnar side of the fifth metacarpal. Often this muscle has a shiny tendon, which helps in its identification.

Muscles of the Medial Surface

1. The **biceps brachii** is a large spindle-shaped muscle medial to the brachialis on the anterior surface of the humerus (see the figure **Medial surface of the forelimb of the cat**). Pull back the cut ends of the pectoral muscles to get a good view of the biceps. This muscle is much more prominent in humans,

but its origin, insertion, and action are very similar in cats and in humans. Follow the muscle to its origin.

Does the biceps have two heads in the cat? _____

2. The broad, flat, exceedingly thin muscle on the posteromedial surface of the arm is the **epitrochlearis**. Its tendon originates from the fascia of the latissimus dorsi, and the muscle inserts into the olecranon of the ulna. This muscle extends the forearm of the cat; it is not found in humans.

3. The **coracobrachialis** (not illustrated) of the cat is insignificant (approximately 1.3 cm, or ½ inch, long) and can be seen as a very small muscle crossing the ventral aspect of the shoulder joint. It runs beneath the biceps brachii to insert on the humerus and has the same function as the human coracobrachialis.

4. Turn the cat so that the ventral forearm muscles (mostly flexors and pronators) can be observed (refer to the **Medial surface of the forelimb . . .** figure). As in humans, most of these muscles arise from the medial epicondyle of the humerus. The **pronator teres** runs from the medial epicondyle of the humerus and declines in size as it approaches its insertion on the radius. Do not bother to trace it to its insertion.

5. Like its human counterpart, the **flexor carpi radialis** runs from the medial epicondyle of the humerus to insert into the second and third metacarpals.

6. The large flat muscle in the center of the medial surface is the **palmaris longus**. Its origin on the medial epicondyle of the

humerus abuts that of the pronator teres and is shared with the flexor carpi radialis. The palmaris longus extends down the forearm to terminate in four tendons on the digits. This muscle is proportionately larger in cats than in humans.

The **flexor carpi ulnaris** arises from a two-headed origin (medial epicondyle of the humerus and olecranon of the ulna).

Its two bellies pass downward to the wrist, where they are united by a single tendon that inserts into the carpals of the wrist. As in humans, this muscle flexes the wrist.

7. If this activity concludes your laboratory session, follow the cleanup instructions in the accompanying box.

Preparing the Dissection Animal for Storage

1. To prevent the internal organs from drying out, dampen a layer of folded paper towels with embalming fluid, and wrap them snugly around the animal's torso. (Do not use *water-soaked* paper towels, which encourages mold growth.) Make sure the dissected areas are completely enveloped.

2. Return the animal's skin flaps to their normal position over the ventral cavity body organs.

3. Place the animal in a plastic storage bag. Add more embalming fluid if necessary, press out excess air, and securely close the bag with a rubber band or twine.

4. Make sure your name tag is securely attached, and place the animal in the designated storage container.

5. Clean all dissecting equipment with soapy water, rinse, and dry it for return to the storage area. Wash down the lab bench, and properly dispose of organic debris and your gloves before leaving the laboratory. Return safety glasses to the appropriate location.

Activity

Dissecting Hindlimb Muscles

Remove the fat and fascia from all thigh surfaces, but do not cut through or remove the **fascia lata** (or iliotibial band), which is a tough white aponeurosis covering the anterolateral surface of the thigh from the hip to the leg. If the cat is a male, the cordlike sperm duct will be embedded in the fat near the pubic symphysis. Carefully clear around, but not in, this region.

Posterolateral Hindlimb Muscles

1. Turn the cat on its ventral surface, and identify the following superficial muscles of the hip and thigh (refer to the figure **Muscles of the posterolateral thigh in the cat**). Viewing the lateral aspect of the hindlimb, you

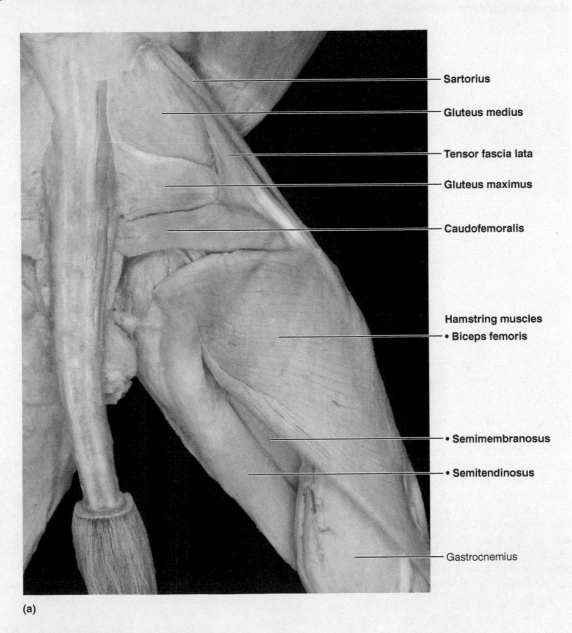

Sartorius

Gluteus medius

Tensor fascia lata

Gluteus maximus

Caudofemoralis

Hamstring muscles
• Biceps femoris

• Semimembranosus

• Semitendinosus

Gastrocnemius

(a)

Muscles of the posterolateral thigh in the cat. (a) Superficial view.

Credits: Illustration: Imagineering STA Media Services; photo: Shawn Miller (dissection) and Mark Nielsen (photography), Pearson Education.

→

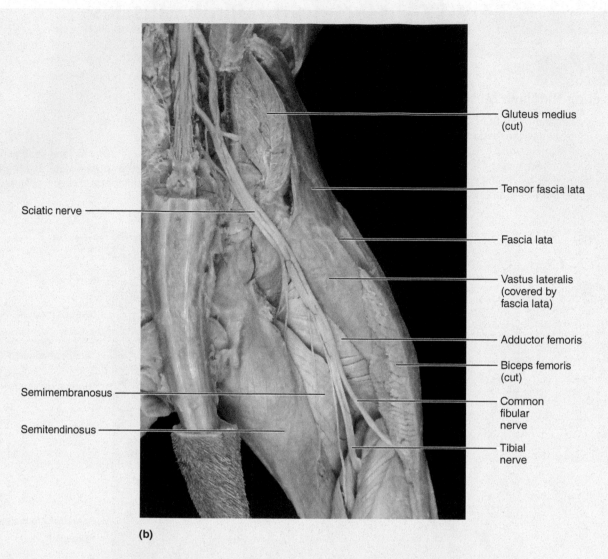

Sciatic nerve

Semimembranosus

Semitendinosus

Gluteus medius (cut)

Tensor fascia lata

Fascia lata

Vastus lateralis (covered by fascia lata)

Adductor femoris

Biceps femoris (cut)

Common fibular nerve

Tibial nerve

(b)

Muscles of the posterolateral thigh in the cat (*continued*) (b) Deep muscles.

Photo credits: Shawn Miller (dissection) and Mark Nielsen (photography), Pearson Education.

will identify these muscles in sequence from the anterior to the posterior aspects of the hip and thigh. Most anterior is the **sartorius**, seen in this view as a thin band (see **Muscles of the posterolateral thigh . . .** figure, Part A). Approximately 4 cm (1½ inches) wide, it extends around the lateral aspect of the thigh to the anterior surface, where the major portion of it lies (see the figure **Superficial muscles of the anteromedial thigh**, Part A). Free it from the adjacent muscles and pass a blunt probe under it to trace its origin and insertion. Homologous to the sartorius muscle in humans, it adducts and rotates the thigh, but in addition, the cat sartorius acts as a knee extensor. Transect this muscle.

2. The **tensor fascia lata** is posterior to the sartorius. It is wide at its superior end, where it originates on the iliac crest, and narrows as it approaches its insertion into the fascia lata, which runs to the proximal tibial region. Transect its superior end and pull it back to expose the **gluteus medius** lying beneath it. This is the largest of the gluteus muscles in the cat. It originates on the ilium and inserts on the greater trochanter of the femur. The gluteus medius overlays and obscures the gluteus

minimus, pyriformis, and gemellus muscles, which will not be identified here.

3. The **gluteus maximus** is a small triangular hip muscle posterior to the superior end of the tensor fasciae latae and paralleling it. In humans the gluteus maximus is a large fleshy muscle forming most of the buttock mass. In the cat it is only about 1.3 cm (½ inch) wide and 5 cm (2 inches) long, and it is smaller than the gluteus medius. The gluteus maximus covers part of the gluteus medius as it extends from the sacral region to the end of the femur. It abducts the thigh.

4. Posterior to the gluteus maximus, identify the triangular **caudofemoralis**, which originates on the caudal vertebrae and inserts into the patella via an aponeurosis. There is no homologue to this muscle in humans; in cats it abducts the thigh and flexes the vertebral column.

5. The **hamstring muscles** of the hindlimb include the biceps femoris, the semitendinosus, and the semimembranosus muscles. The **biceps femoris** is a large, powerful muscle that covers about three-fourths of the posterolateral surface of the

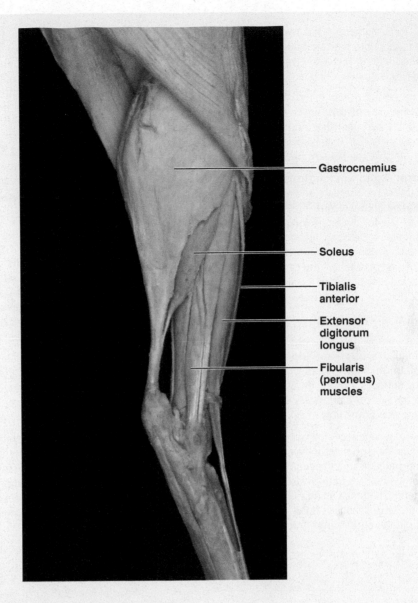

— **Gastrocnemius**

— **Soleus**

— **Tibialis anterior**

— **Extensor digitorum longus**

— **Fibularis (peroneus) muscles**

Superficial muscles of the posterolateral aspect of the shank (leg).

Credits: Illustration: Imagineering STA Media Services; photo: Shawn Miller (dissection) and Mark Nielsen (photography), Pearson Education.

thigh. It is 4 cm (1½ inches) to 5 cm (2 inches) wide throughout its length. Trace it from its origin on the ischial tuberosity to its insertion on the tibia. Part of the **semitendinosus** can be seen beneath the posterior border of the biceps femoris. Transect and reflect the biceps muscle to reveal the whole length of the semitendinosus and the large sciatic nerve positioned under the biceps (see **Muscles of the posterolateral thigh . . .** fig-ure, Part B). Contrary to what its name implies ("half-tendon"), this muscle is muscular and fleshy except at its insertion. It is uniformly about 2 cm (¾ inch) wide as it runs down the thigh from the ischial tuberosity to the medial side of the tibia. It flexes the knee. The **semimembranosus**, a large muscle lying medial to the semitendinosus and largely obscured by it, is best seen in an anterior view of the thigh (see **Superficial muscles of the anteromedial thigh** figure, Part B). If desired, however, the semitendinosus can be transected to view it from the pos-terior aspect. The semimembranosus is larger and broader than the semitendinosus. Like the other hamstrings, it originates on

the ischial tuberosity and inserts on the medial epicondyle of the femur and the medial tibial surface.

How does the semimembranosus compare with its human homologue?

_____

_____

6. Remove the heavy fascia covering the lateral surface of the shank (leg). Moving from the posterior to the anterior aspect, identify the following muscles on the posterolateral shank (see the figure **Superficial muscles of the posterolateral aspect of the shank (leg)**). First reflect the lower portion of the biceps femoris to see the origin of the **triceps surae**, the large com-posite muscle of the calf. Humans also have a triceps surae. The **gastrocnemius**, part of the triceps surae, is the largest muscle

on the shank. As in humans, it has two heads and inserts via the calcaneal tendon into the calcaneus. Run a probe beneath this muscle and then transect it to reveal the **soleus**, which is deep to the gastrocnemius.

7. Another important group of muscles in the leg is the **fibularis (peroneus) muscles**, which collectively appear as a slender, evenly shaped superficial muscle lying anterior to the triceps surae. Originating on the fibula and inserting on the digits and metatarsals, the fibularis muscles flex the foot.

8. The **extensor digitorum longus** lies anterior to the fibularis muscles. Its origin, insertion, and action in cats are similar to the homologous human muscle. The **tibialis anterior** is anterior to the extensor digitorum longus. The tibialis anterior is roughly triangular in cross section and heavier at its proximal end. Locate its origin on the proximal fibula and tibia and its insertion on the first metatarsal. You can see the sharp edge of the tibia at the anterior border of this muscle. As in humans, it is a foot flexor.

Anteromedial Hindlimb Muscles

1. Turn the cat onto its dorsal surface to identify the muscles of the anteromedial hindlimb (see **Superficial muscles of the anteromedial thigh** figure). Note once again the straplike sartorius at the surface of the thigh, which you have already identified and transected. It originates on the ilium and inserts on the medial region of the tibia.

2. Reflect the cut ends of the sartorius to identify the **quadriceps** muscles. The most medial muscle of this group, the **vastus medialis**, lies just beneath the sartorius. Resting close to the femur, it arises from the ilium and inserts into the patellar ligament. The small spindle-shaped muscle anterior and lateral to the vastus medialis is the **rectus femoris**, In cats this muscle originates entirely from the femur.

What is the origin of the rectus femoris in humans?

_____

_____

Free the rectus femoris from the most lateral muscle of this group, the large, fleshy **vastus lateralis**, which lies deep to the tensor fascia lata. The vastus lateralis arises from the lateral femoral surface and inserts, along with the other vasti muscles, into the patellar ligament. Transect this muscle to identify the deep **vastus intermedius**, the smallest of the vasti muscles. It lies medial to the vastus lateralis and merges superiorly with the vastus medialis. The vastus intermedius is not shown in the figure.

3. The **gracilis** is a broad thin muscle that covers the posterior portion of the medial aspect of the thigh (see **Superficial muscles of the anteromedial thigh** figure, Part A). It originates on the pubic symphysis and inserts on the medial proximal tibial surface. In cats the gracilis adducts the leg and draws it posteriorly.

How does this compare with the human gracilis?

_____

_____

4. Free and transect the gracilis to view the adductor muscles deep to it. The **adductor femoris** is a large muscle that lies beneath the gracilis and abuts the semimembranosus medially. Its origin is the pubic ramus and the ischium, and its fibers pass downward to insert on most of the length of the femoral shaft. The adductor femoris is homologous to the human *adductor magnus*, and *adductor brevis*. Its function is to extend the thigh after it has been drawn forward, and to adduct the thigh. A small muscle about 2.5 cm (1 inch) long—the **adductor longus**—touches the superior margin of the adductor femoris. It originates on the pubis and inserts on the proximal surface of the femur.

5. Before continuing your dissection, locate the **femoral triangle**, an important area bordered by the proximal edge of the sartorius and the adductor muscles. It is usually possible to identify the femoral artery (injected with red latex) and the femoral vein (injected with blue latex), which span the triangle (see **Superficial muscles of the anteromedial thigh** figure, Part A). (You will identify these vessels again in your study of the circulatory system.) If your instructor wishes you to identify the pectineus and iliopsoas, remove these vessels and go on to steps 6 and 7.

6. Examine the superolateral margin of the adductor longus to locate the small **pectineus**. It is sometimes covered by the gracilis (which you have cut and reflected). The pectineus, which originates on the pubis and inserts on the proximal end of the femur, is similar in all ways to its human homologue.

7. Just lateral to the pectineus you can see a small portion of the **iliopsoas**, a long and cylindrical muscle. Its origin is on the transverse processes of T_1 through T_{12} and the lumbar vertebrae, and it passes posteriorly toward the body wall to insert on the medial aspect of the proximal femur. The iliopsoas flexes and laterally rotates the thigh. It corresponds to the human iliopsoas.

8. Reidentify the gastrocnemius of the shank and then the **plantaris**, which is fused with the lateral head of the gastrocnemius (see the figure **Superficial muscles of the anteromedial shank (leg) of the cat**). It originates from the lateral aspect of the femur and patella, and its tendon passes around the calcaneus to insert on the second phalanx. Working with the triceps surae, it flexes the digits and extends the foot.

9. Anterior to the plantaris is the **flexor digitorum longus**, a long, tapering muscle with two heads. It originates on the lateral surfaces of the proximal fibula and tibia and inserts via four tendons into the terminal phalanges. As in humans, it flexes the toes.

10. The **tibialis posterior** is a long, flat muscle lateral and deep to the flexor digitorum longus (not shown in the **figure**). It originates on the medial surface of the head of the fibula and the ventral tibia. It merges with a flat, shiny tendon to insert into the tarsals.

11. The **flexor hallucis longus** (also not illustrated) is a long muscle that lies lateral to the tibialis posterior. It originates from the posterior tibia and passes downward to the ankle. It is a uniformly broad muscle in the cat. As in humans, it is a flexor of the great toe.

12. If this activity concludes your laboratory session, follow the cleanup instructions in the accompanying box.

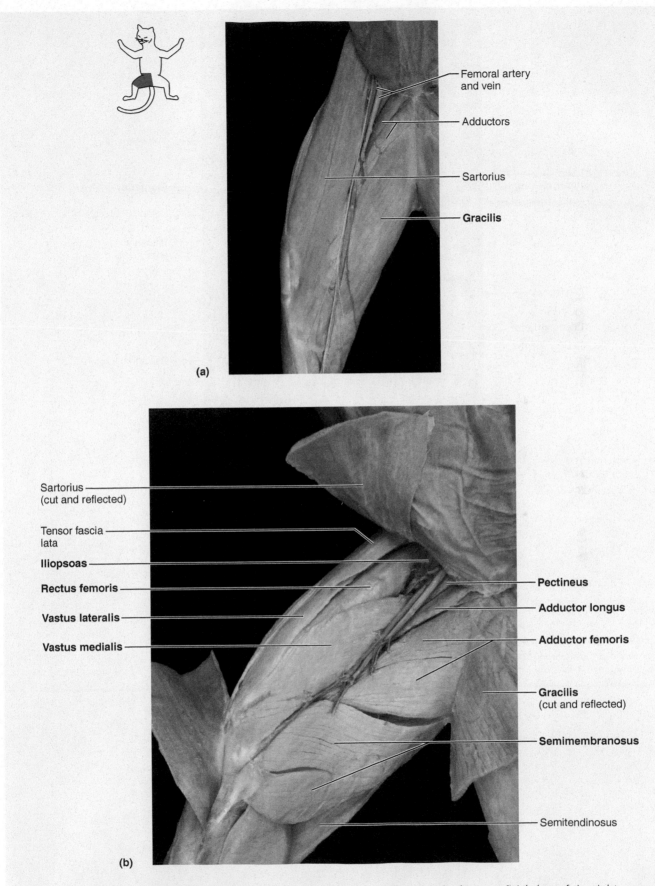

(a)

- Femoral artery and vein
- Adductors
- Sartorius
- **Gracilis**

Sartorius (cut and reflected)

Tensor fascia lata

Iliopsoas

Rectus femoris

Vastus lateralis

Vastus medialis

(b)

- **Pectineus**
- **Adductor longus**
- **Adductor femoris**
- **Gracilis** (cut and reflected)
- **Semimembranosus**
- Semitendinosus

Superficial muscles of the anteromedial thigh. (a) Gracilis and sartorius are intact in this superficial view of the right thigh. **(b)** The gracilis and sartorius are transected and reflected to show deeper muscles.

Credits: Illustration: Imagineering STA Media Services; photos: Shawn Miller (dissection) and Mark Nielsen (photography), Pearson Education.

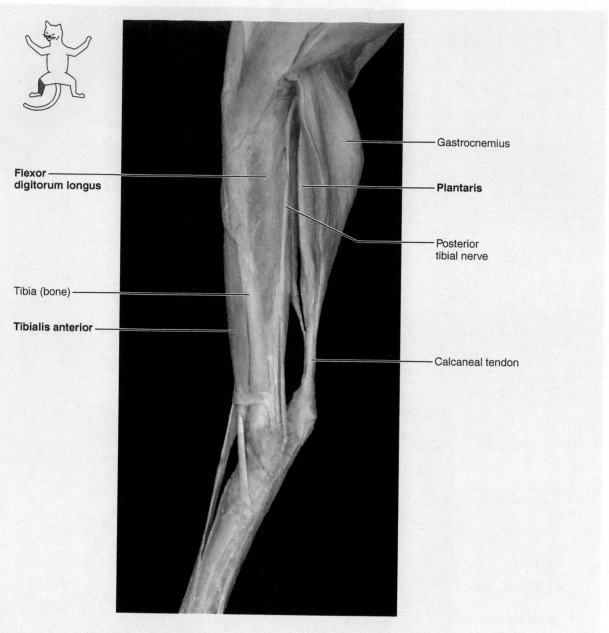

Gastrocnemius

Flexor digitorum longus

Plantaris

Posterior tibial nerve

Tibia (bone)

Tibialis anterior

Calcaneal tendon

Superficial muscles of the anteromedial shank (leg) of the cat.

Credits: Illustration: Imagineering STA Media Services; photo: Shawn Miller (dissection) and Mark Nielsen (photography), Pearson Education.

Preparing the Dissection Animal for Storage

1. To prevent the internal organs from drying out, dampen a layer of folded paper towels with embalming fluid, and wrap them snugly around the animal's torso. (Do not use *water-soaked* paper towels, which encourages mold growth.) Make sure the dissected areas are completely enveloped.

2. Return the animal's skin flaps to their normal position over the ventral cavity body organs.

3. Place the animal in a plastic storage bag. Add more embalming fluid if necessary, press out excess air, and securely close the bag with a rubber band or twine.

4. Make sure your name tag is securely attached, and place the animal in the designated storage container.

5. Clean all dissecting equipment with soapy water, rinse, and dry it for return to the storage area. Wash down the lab bench, and properly dispose of organic debris and your gloves before leaving the laboratory. Return safety glasses to the appropriate location.

Dissection and Identification of Cat Muscles

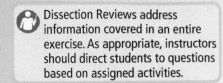

Dissection Reviews address information covered in an entire exercise. As appropriate, instructors should direct students to questions based on assigned activities.

Many human muscles are modified from those of the cat (or any quadruped). The following questions refer to these differences.

1. How does the human trapezius muscle differ from the cat's?

_____

2. How does the deltoid differ?

_____

_____

3. How does the biceps brachii differ?

_____

_____

4. How do the size and orientation of the human gluteus maximus muscle differ from that in the cat?

_____

_____

_____

5. How does the origin of the rectus femoris in the cat differ from that in humans?

_____

_____

6. Explain how the tendinous intersections of the rectus abdominis of the cat differ from those found in humans.

_____

7. Match each term in column B to its description in column A.

Column A	Column B
_____ 1. to separate muscles	a. dissect
_____ 2. to fold back a muscle	b. embalm
_____ 3. to cut through a muscle	c. reflect
_____ 4. to preserve tissue	d. transect

Dissection of Cat Spinal Nerves

Learning Outcome

▶ Identify on a dissected animal the musculocutaneous, radial, median, and ulnar nerves of the forelimb and the femoral, saphenous, sciatic, common fibular (peroneal), and tibial nerves of the hindlimb.

Materials

▶ Disposable gloves
▶ Safety glasses
▶ Dissecting instruments and tray
▶ Animal specimen from previous dissection
▶ Embalming fluid
▶ Paper towels
▶ Organic debris container

The cat has 38 or 39 pairs of spinal nerves compared to 31 in humans. Of these, 8 are cervical, 13 thoracic, 7 lumbar, 3 sacral, and 7 or 8 caudal. A complete dissection of the cat's spinal nerves would be extraordinarily time-consuming and is not warranted in a basic anatomy and physiology course. However, it is desirable for you to have some dissection work to complement your study of the anatomical charts. Refer to a discussion of human spinal nerves as you work.

Go to Mastering A&P™ **> Study Area to improve your performance in A&P Lab.**

> Animations & Videos > Cat Dissection Videos > The Brachial Plexus

Instructors may assign Cat Dissection Videos, Practice Anatomy Lab Practical questions (PAL) for the dissections, and more using the Mastering A&P™ Item Library.

Dissection of Cat Spinal Nerves
ACTIVITY Dissecting Nerves of the Brachial Plexus

Dissecting Nerves of the Brachial Plexus

1. Don disposable gloves and safety glasses. Place your cat specimen on the dissecting tray, dorsal side down. Reflect the cut ends of the left pectoralis muscles to expose the large brachial plexus in the axillary region (see the figure **Brachial plexus and major blood vessels of the left forelimb of the cat, ventral aspect**). Use forceps to carefully clear away the connective tissue around the exposed nerves as far back toward their points of origin as possible.

2. The **musculocutaneous nerve** is the most superior nerve of this group. It splits into two subdivisions that run under the margins of the coracobrachialis and biceps brachii muscles. Trace its fibers into the ventral muscles of the arm it serves.

3. Locate the large **radial nerve** inferior to the musculocutaneous nerve. The radial nerve serves the dorsal muscles of the arm and forearm. Follow it into the three heads of the triceps brachii muscle.

4. In the cat, the **median nerve** is closely associated with the brachial artery and vein (see **Brachial plexus . . .** figure). It travels through the arm to supply the ventral muscles of the forearm (with the exception of the flexor carpi ulnaris and the ulnar head of the flexor digitorum profundus). It also innervates some of the intrinsic hand muscles, as in humans. Locate and follow it to the ventral forearm muscles.

5. The **ulnar nerve** is the most posterior of the large brachial plexus nerves. Follow it as it travels down the forelimb, passing over the medial epicondyle of the humerus, to supply the flexor carpi ulnaris, the ulnar head of the flexor digitorum profundus, and the hand muscles.

6. If this activity concludes your laboratory session, follow the cleanup instructions in the accompanying box.

Preparing the Dissection Animal for Storage

1. To prevent the internal organs from drying out, dampen a layer of folded paper towels with embalming fluid, and wrap them snugly around the animal's torso. (Do not use *water-soaked* paper towels, which encourages mold growth.) Make sure the dissected areas are completely enveloped.

2. Return the animal's skin flaps to their normal position over the ventral cavity body organs.

3. Place the animal in a plastic storage bag. Add more embalming fluid if necessary, press out excess air, and securely close the bag with a rubber band or twine.

4. Make sure your name tag is securely attached, and place the animal in the designated storage container.

5. Clean all dissecting equipment with soapy water, rinse, and dry it for return to the storage area. Wash down the lab bench, and properly dispose of organic debris and your gloves before leaving the laboratory. Return safety glasses to the appropriate location.

Dissection of Cat Spinal Nerves
Activity Dissecting Nerves of the Brachial Plexus

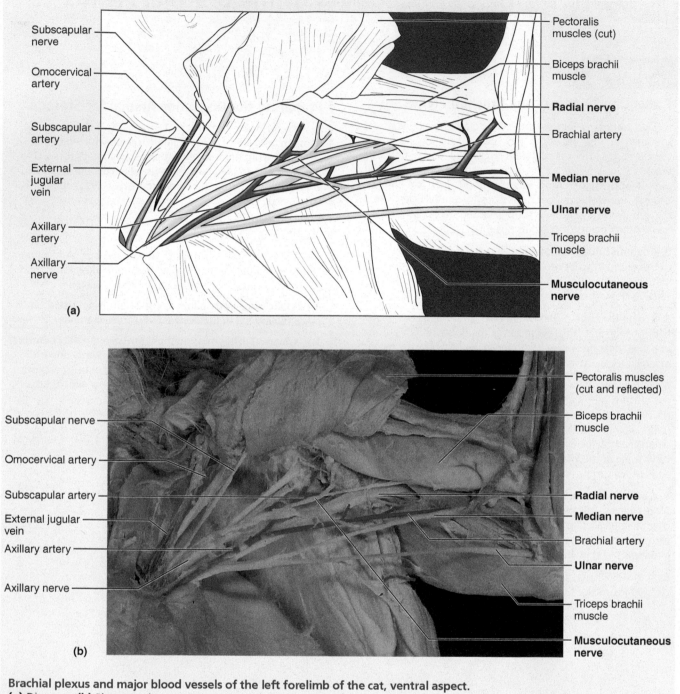

Brachial plexus and major blood vessels of the left forelimb of the cat, ventral aspect.
(a) Diagram. **(b)** Photograph.

Credits: Illustration a: Kristin Mount; photo b: Paul Waring, Pearson Education.

Dissection of Cat Spinal Nerves
ACTIVITY Dissecting Nerves of the Lumbosacral Plexus

Activity

Dissecting Nerves of the Lumbosacral Plexus

1. To locate the **femoral nerve** arising from the lumbar plexus, first identify the *femoral triangle*, which is bordered by the sartorius and adductor muscles of the anterior thigh (see the figure **Lumbar plexus of the cat, ventral aspect**). The large femoral nerve travels through this region after emerging from the psoas major muscle in close association with the femoral artery and vein. Follow the nerve into the muscles and skin of the anterior thigh, which it supplies. Notice also its cutaneous branch in the cat, the **saphenous nerve**, which continues down the anterior medial surface of the thigh with the great saphenous artery and vein to supply the skin of the anterior shank and foot.

2. Turn the cat ventral side down so you can view the posterior aspect of the lower limb (see the figure **Sacral plexus of the cat, dorsal aspect**). Reflect the ends of the transected biceps femoris muscle to view the large cordlike sciatic nerve. The **sciatic nerve** arises from the sacral plexus and serves the dorsal thigh muscles and all the muscles of the leg and foot. Follow the nerve as it travels down the posterior thigh lateral to the semimembranosus muscle. Note that just superior to the gastrocnemius muscle of the calf, it divides into its two major branches, which serve the leg.

3. Identify the **tibial nerve** medially and the **common fibular (peroneal) nerve**, which curves over the lateral surface of the gastrocnemius.

4. If this activity concludes your laboratory session, follow the cleanup instructions in the accompanying box.

Preparing the Dissection Animal for Storage

1. To prevent the internal organs from drying out, dampen a layer of folded paper towels with embalming fluid, and wrap them snugly around the animal's torso. (Do not use *water-soaked* paper towels, which encourages mold growth.) Make sure the dissected areas are completely enveloped.

2. Return the animal's skin flaps to their normal position over the ventral cavity body organs.

3. Place the animal in a plastic storage bag. Add more embalming fluid if necessary, press out excess air, and securely close the bag with a rubber band or twine.

4. Make sure your name tag is securely attached, and place the animal in the designated storage container.

5. Clean all dissecting equipment with soapy water, rinse, and dry it for return to the storage area. Wash down the lab bench, and properly dispose of organic debris and your gloves before leaving the laboratory. Return safety glasses to the appropriate location.

From Dissection Exercise 2, Activity 2, of *Human Anatomy & Physiology Laboratory Manual, Cat Version* Thirteenth Edition. Elaine N. Marieb and Lori Smith. Copyright © 2019 by Pearson Education, Inc. All rights reserved.

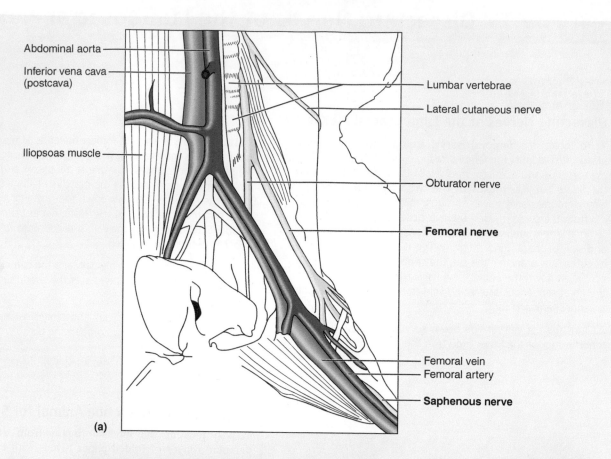

Abdominal aorta

Inferior vena cava
(postcava)

Iliopsoas muscle

Lumbar vertebrae

Lateral cutaneous nerve

Obturator nerve

Femoral nerve

Femoral vein
Femoral artery

Saphenous nerve

(a)

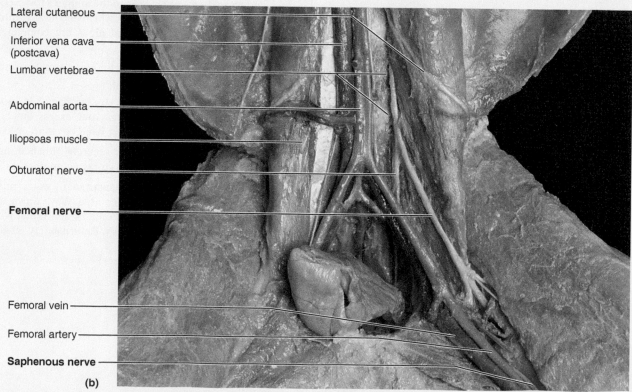

Lateral cutaneous
nerve

Inferior vena cava
(postcava)

Lumbar vertebrae

Abdominal aorta

Iliopsoas muscle

Obturator nerve

Femoral nerve

Femoral vein

Femoral artery

Saphenous nerve

(b)

Lumbar plexus of the cat, ventral aspect. (a) Diagram. **(b)** Photograph.

Credits: Illustration a: Kristin Mount; photo b: Elena Dorfman, Pearson Education.

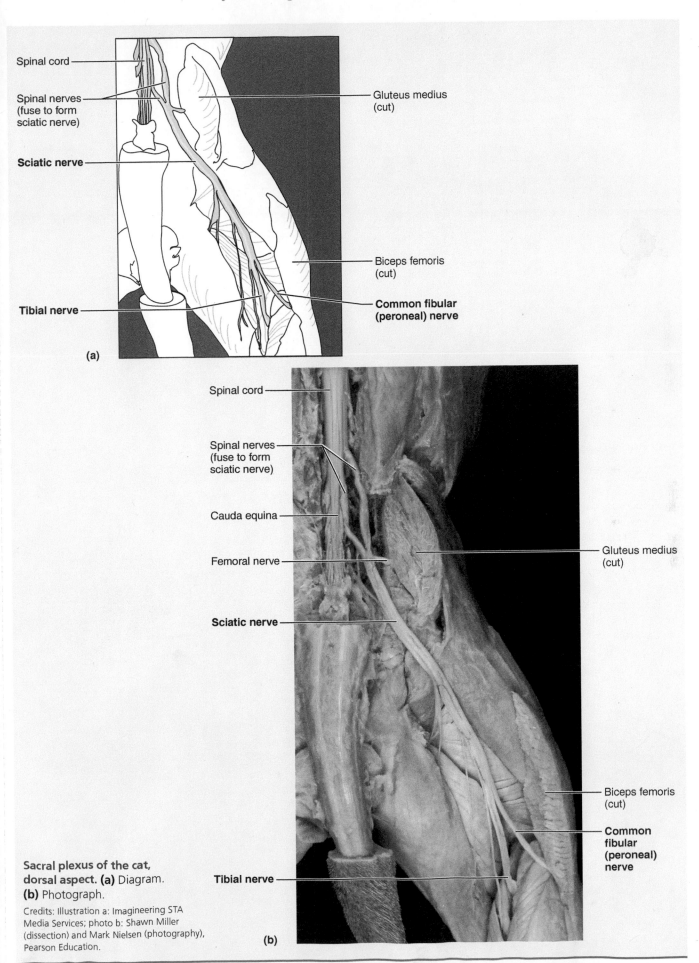

Spinal cord

Spinal nerves
(fuse to form
sciatic nerve)

Sciatic nerve

Gluteus medius
(cut)

Biceps femoris
(cut)

Tibial nerve

**Common fibular
(peroneal) nerve**

(a)

Spinal cord

Spinal nerves
(fuse to form
sciatic nerve)

Cauda equina

Femoral nerve

Gluteus medius
(cut)

Sciatic nerve

Biceps femoris
(cut)

**Common
fibular
(peroneal)
nerve**

Tibial nerve

(b)

**Sacral plexus of the cat,
dorsal aspect. (a)** Diagram.
(b) Photograph.

Credits: Illustration a: Imagineering STA
Media Services; photo b: Shawn Miller
(dissection) and Mark Nielsen (photography),
Pearson Education.

Dissection of Cat
Spinal Nerves

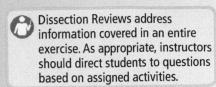

1. From anterior to posterior, put in their proper order the nerves issuing from the brachial plexus (i.e., the median, musculocutaneous, radial, and ulnar nerves).

   _____

   _____

2. Which of the nerves named above serves most of the cat's forearm extensor muscles? _____ Which serves the

   forearm flexors? _____

3. Just superior to the gastrocnemius muscle, the sciatic nerve divides into its two main branches, the _____

   and _____ nerves.

4. What name is given to the cutaneous nerve of the cat's thigh? _____

Identification of Selected Endocrine Organs of the Cat

Learning Outcomes

▶ Prepare the cat for observation by opening the ventral body cavity.

▶ Identify and name the major endocrine organs on a dissected cat.

Materials

▶ Disposable gloves

▶ Safety glasses

▶ Dissecting instruments and tray

▶ Animal specimen from previous dissections

▶ Bone cutters

▶ Embalming fluid

▶ Paper towels

▶ Organic debris container

Go to Mastering A&P™ **> Study Area to improve your performance in A&P Lab.**

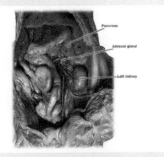

> Lab Tools > Practice Anatomy Lab > Cat > Endocrine System

Instructors may assign Cat Dissection Videos, Practice Anatomy Lab Practical questions (PAL) for the dissections, and more using the Mastering A&P™ Item Library.

Identification of Selected Endocrine Organs of the Cat
ACTIVITY Opening the Ventral Body Cavity

Opening the Ventral Body Cavity

1. Don gloves and safety glasses, and then obtain your dissection animal. Place the animal on the dissecting tray, ventral side up. Using scissors, make a longitudinal median incision through the ventral body wall. Begin your cut just superior to the midline of the pubis, and continue it anteriorly to the rib cage. Check the incision guide provided in the figure **Incisions to be made in opening the ventral body cavity of a cat** as you work.

2. Angle the scissors slightly (1.3 cm, or ½ inch) to the right or left of the sternum, and continue the cut through the rib cartilages (just lateral to the body midline), to the base of the throat. Your instructor may have you use heavier bone cutters to cut through the rib cartilages.

3. Make two lateral cuts on both sides of the ventral body surface, anterior and posterior to the diaphragm, which separates the thoracic and abdominal parts of the ventral body cavity. *Leave the diaphragm intact.* Spread the thoracic walls laterally to expose the thoracic organs.

4. Make an angled lateral cut on each side of the median incision line just superior to the pubis, and spread the flaps to expose the abdominal cavity organs.

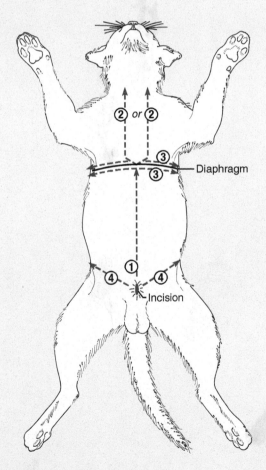

Incisions to be made in opening the ventral body cavity of a cat.
Numbers indicate sequence.
Credit: Precision Graphics.

Activity

Identifying Organs

The **Ventral body organs of the cat** figure provides a general overview to guide you in identifying the most important organs and those that will help you to locate the desired endocrine organs (marked *). As you work, also examine the **Endocrine organs in the cat** figure; the schematic and photographic images show the relative positioning of several of the animal's endocrine organs.

Neck and Thoracic Cavity Organs

Trachea: The windpipe; runs down the midline of the throat and then divides just anterior to the lungs to form the bronchi, which plunge into the lungs on either side.

*Thyroid gland: Its dark lobes straddle the trachea (see Part B of **Endocrine organs . . .** figure). Thyroid hormones are the main hormones regulating the body's metabolic rate. In general, the metabolic rate of a species of animal is inversely proportional to its size.

*Thymus: Glandular structure superior to and partly covering the heart (see Part B of **Endocrine organs . . .** figure). The hormones of the thymus are intimately involved in programming the immune system. If you have a young cat, the thymus will be quite large. In old cats, most of this organ has been replaced by fat.

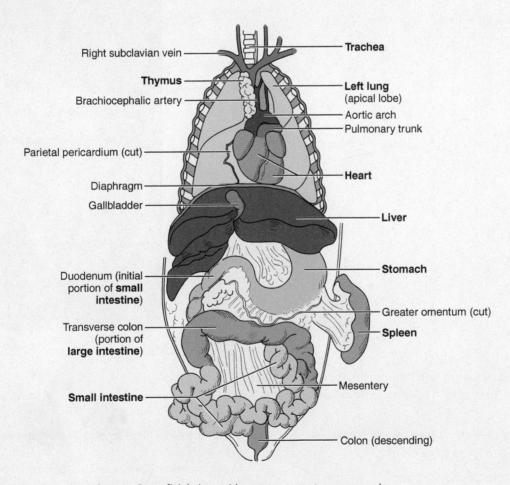

Right subclavian vein — Trachea
Thymus — Left lung (apical lobe)
Brachiocephalic artery — Aortic arch — Pulmonary trunk
Parietal pericardium (cut) — Heart
Diaphragm —
Gallbladder — Liver
Stomach
Duodenum (initial portion of **small intestine**) — Greater omentum (cut) — Spleen
Transverse colon (portion of **large intestine**) — Mesentery
Small intestine — Colon (descending)

Ventral body cavity organs of the cat. Superficial view with greater omentum removed.
Credit: Kristin Mount.

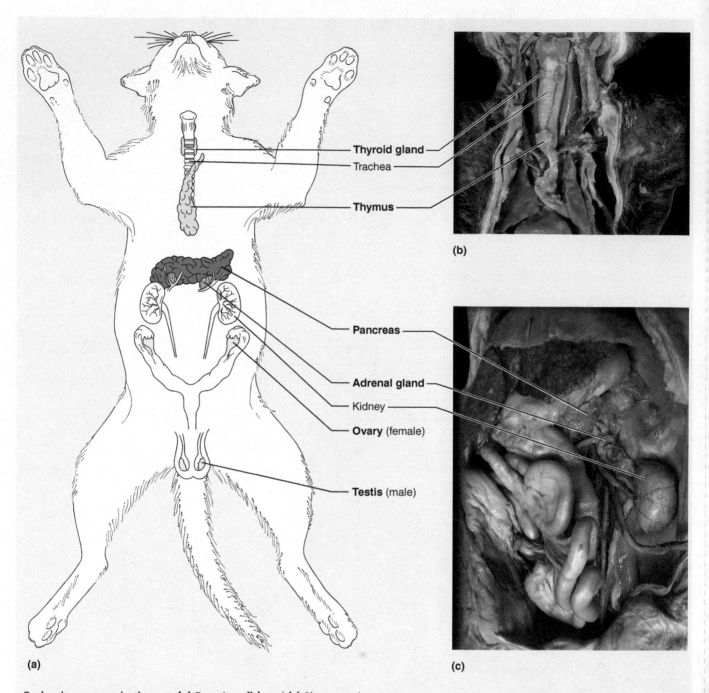

Endocrine organs in the cat. (a) Drawing. **(b)** and **(c)** Photographs.

Credits: Illustration a: Precision Graphics; photos b, c: Yvonne Baptiste-Szymanski, Pearson Education.

Heart: In the mediastinum enclosed by the pericardium.

Lungs: Paired organs flanking the heart.

Abdominopelvic Cavity Organs

Liver: Large multilobed organ lying under the umbrella of the diaphragm.

• Lift the drapelike, fat-infiltrated greater omentum covering the abdominal organs to expose the following organs:

Stomach: Dorsally located sac to the left side of the liver.

Spleen: Flattened brown organ curving around the lateral aspect of the stomach.

Small intestine: Tubelike organ continuing posteriorly from the stomach.

Large intestine: Takes a U-shaped course around the small intestine to terminate in the rectum.

• Lift the first section of the small intestine with your forceps to see the pancreas.

*Pancreas: Diffuse gland located in delicate mesentery lying deep to and between the small intestine and stomach (see Part C of **Endocrine organs in the cat** figure). This gland is extremely important in regulating blood sugar levels.

- Push the intestines to one side with a probe to reveal the deeper organs in the abdominal cavity.

Kidneys: Bean-shaped organs located toward the dorsal body wall surface and behind the peritoneum.

*Adrenal glands: Visible above and medial to each kidney, these small glands produce corticosteroids important in the stress response and in preventing abnormalities of water and electrolyte balance in the body (see Part C of **Endocrine organs . . . figure**).

*Gonads (ovaries or testes): Sex organs producing sex hormones. The location of the gonads is illustrated in Part A of **Endocrine organs . . .** figure, but their identification is deferred until the reproductive system organs are considered.

If this activity concludes your laboratory session, follow the cleanup instructions in the accompanying box.

Preparing the Dissection Animal for Storage

1. To prevent the internal organs from drying out, dampen a layer of folded paper towels with embalming fluid, and wrap them snugly around the animal's torso. (Do not use *water-soaked* paper towels, which encourages mold growth.) Make sure the dissected areas are completely enveloped.

2. Return the animal's skin flaps to their normal position over the ventral cavity body organs.

3. Place the animal in a plastic storage bag. Add more embalming fluid if necessary, press out excess air, and securely close the bag with a rubber band or twine.

4. Make sure your name tag is securely attached, and place the animal in the designated storage container.

5. Clean all dissecting equipment with soapy water, rinse, and dry it for return to the storage area. Wash down the lab bench, and properly dispose of organic debris and your gloves before leaving the laboratory. Return safety glasses to the appropriate location.

Identification of Selected Endocrine Organs of the Cat

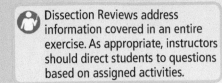

Dissection Reviews address information covered in an entire exercise. As appropriate, instructors should direct students to questions based on assigned activities.

1. How do the locations of the endocrine organs in the cat compare with those in the human?

   _____

   _____

2. Name two endocrine organs located in the neck region: _____ and _____

3. Name three endocrine organs located in the abdominal cavity.

   _____

   _____

4. Given the assumption (not necessarily true) that human beings have more stress than cats, which endocrine organs would you expect to be relatively larger in humans?

   _____

5. Cats are smaller animals than humans. Which would you expect to have a (relatively speaking) more active thyroid gland—cats

   or humans? _____ Why? _____

   _____

   _____

Dissection of the Blood Vessels of the Cat

Learning Outcomes

▶ Identify some of the most important blood vessels of the cat.

▶ Point out anatomical differences between the vascular system of the human and the cat.

Materials

▶ Disposable gloves
▶ Safety glasses
▶ Dissecting instruments and tray
▶ Animal specimen from previous dissections
▶ Bone cutters
▶ Scissors
▶ Embalming fluid
▶ Paper towels
▶ Organic debris container

Go to Mastering A&P™ **> Study Area to improve your performance in A&P Lab.**

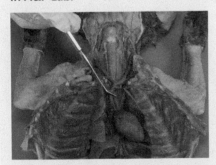

> Animations & Videos > Cat Dissection Videos > Blood Vessels of the Thorax

Instructors may assign Cat Dissection Videos, Practice Anatomy Lab Practical questions (PAL) for the dissections, and more using the Mastering A&P™ Item Library.

Opening the Ventral Body Cavity

If you have not already opened your animal's ventral body cavity, do so now by following your instructor's directions.

Activity

Preliminary Organ Identification

A helpful prelude to identifying and tracing the blood supply of the various organs of the cat is a preliminary identification of ventral body cavity organs. Locate and identify the following body cavity organs; as you work, refer to the figure **Ventral body organs of the cat**.

Thoracic Cavity Organs

Heart: In the mediastinum enclosed by the pericardium.

Lungs: Flanking the heart.

Thymus: Superior to and partially covering the heart. The thymus is quite large in young cats but is largely replaced by fat as cats age.

Abdominal Cavity Organs

Liver: Posterior to the diaphragm.

- Lift the large, drapelike, fat-infiltrated greater omentum covering the abdominal organs to expose the following:

Stomach: Dorsally located and to the left of the liver.

Spleen: A flattened, brown organ curving around the lateral aspect of the stomach.

Small intestine: Continues posteriorly from the stomach.

Large intestine: Takes a U-shaped course around the small intestine and terminates in the rectum.

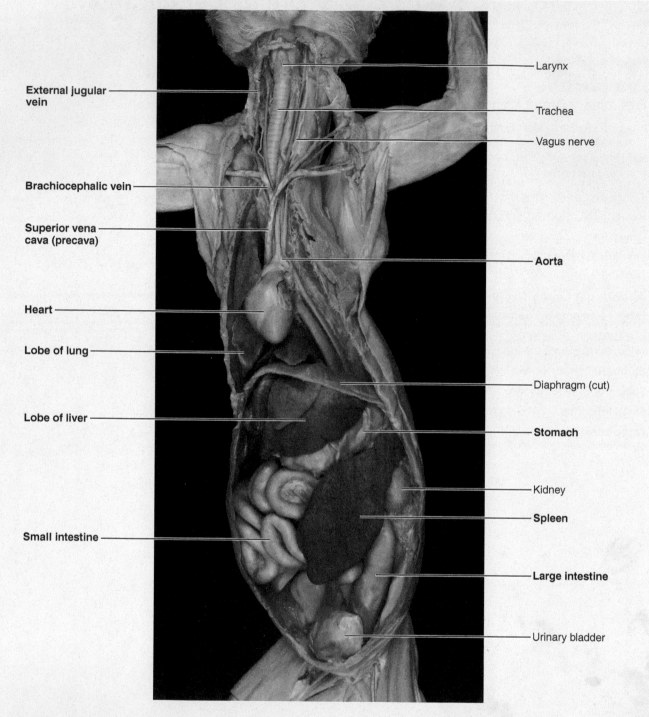

External jugular vein

Brachiocephalic vein

Superior vena cava (precava)

Heart

Lobe of lung

Lobe of liver

Small intestine

Larynx

Trachea

Vagus nerve

Aorta

Diaphragm (cut)

Stomach

Kidney

Spleen

Large intestine

Urinary bladder

Ventral body cavity organs of the cat. (Greater omentum has been removed.)

Photo credits: Shawn Miller (dissection) and Mark Nielsen (photography), Pearson Education.

Activity

Preparing to Identify the Blood Vessels

As you work to identify the blood vessels of the cat, consult a discussion of the anatomy of human blood vessels.

1. Don gloves and safety glasses, and then obtain your dissection animal. Place the animal on the dissection tray, ventral side up. Carefully clear away any thymus tissue or fat obscuring the heart and the large vessels associated with the heart. Before identifying the blood vessels, try to locate the *phrenic nerve* (from the cervical plexus), which innervates the diaphragm. The phrenic nerves lie ventral to the root of the lung on each side as they pass to the diaphragm. Also attempt to locate the *vagus nerve* (cranial nerve X) passing laterally along the trachea and dorsal to the root of the lung.

2. Slit the parietal pericardium and reflect it superiorly. Then, cut it away from its heart attachments. Review the structures of the heart. Notice its pointed inferior end (apex) and its broader superior base. Identify the two *atria*, which appear darker than the inferior *ventricles*.

3. Identify the **aorta**, the largest artery in the body, issuing from the left ventricle. Also identify the *coronary arteries* in the sulcus on the ventral surface of the heart. As an aid to blood vessel identification, the arteries of laboratory dissection specimens are injected with red latex; the veins are injected with blue latex. Exceptions to this will be noted as they are encountered.

4. Identify the two large venae cavae—the **superior** and **inferior venae cavae**—entering the right atrium. The superior vena cava is the largest dark-colored vessel entering the base of the heart. These vessels are called the precava and postcava, respectively, in the cat. The caval veins drain the same relative body areas as in humans. Also identify the **pulmonary trunk** (usually injected with blue latex) extending anteriorly from the right ventricle. The right and left pulmonary arteries branch off of the pulmonary trunk. Trace the **pulmonary arteries** until they enter the lungs. Locate the **pulmonary veins** entering the left atrium and the ascending aorta arising from the left ventricle and running dorsal to the precava and to the left of the body midline.

Activity

Identifying the Arteries of the Cat

Begin your dissection of the arterial system of the cat. Refer to the figures **Arterial system of the cat** and **Cat dissected to reveal major blood vessels**.

1. Reidentify the aorta as it emerges from the left ventricle. The first branches of the aorta are the **coronary arteries**, which supply the myocardium. The coronary arteries emerge from the base of the aorta and can be seen on the surface of the heart. Follow the aorta as it arches (aortic arch), and identify its major branches. In the cat, the aortic arch gives off two large vessels, the **brachiocephalic artery** and the **left subclavian artery**. The brachiocephalic artery has three major branches, the right subclavian artery and the right and left common carotid arteries. Note that in humans, the left common carotid artery directly branches off the aortic arch.

2. Follow the **right common carotid artery** along the right side of the trachea as it moves anteriorly, giving off branches to the neck muscles, thyroid gland, and trachea. At the level of the larynx, it branches to form the **external** and **internal carotid arteries**. The internal carotid is quite small in the cat and it may be difficult to locate. It may even be absent. The distribution of the carotid arteries parallels that in humans.

3. Follow the **right subclavian artery** laterally. It gives off four branches, the first being the tiny **vertebral artery**, which along with the internal carotid artery provides the arterial circulation of the brain. Other branches of the subclavian artery include the **costocervical trunk** (to the costal and cervical regions), the **thyrocervical trunk** (to the shoulder), and the **internal thoracic (mammary) artery** (serving the ventral thoracic wall). As the subclavian passes in front of the first rib it becomes the **axillary artery**. Its branches, which may be difficult to identify, supply the trunk and shoulder muscles. These are the **ventral thoracic artery** (to the pectoral muscles), the **long thoracic artery** (to pectoral muscles and latissimus dorsi), and the **subscapular artery** (to the trunk muscles). As the axillary artery enters the arm, it is called the **brachial artery**, and it travels with the median nerve down the length of the humerus. At the elbow, the brachial artery branches to produce the two major arteries serving the forearm and hand, the **radial** and **ulnar arteries**.

4. Return to the thorax, lift the left lung, and follow the course of the *descending aorta* through the thoracic cavity. The esophagus overlies it along its course. Notice the paired **intercostal arteries** that branch laterally from the aorta in the thoracic region.

5. Follow the aorta through the diaphragm into the abdominal cavity. Carefully pull the peritoneum away from its ventral surface and identify the following vessels:

Celiac trunk: The first branch diverging from the aorta immediately as it enters the abdominal cavity; supplies the stomach, liver, gallbladder, pancreas, and spleen. (Trace as many of its branches to these organs as possible.)

Superior mesenteric artery: Immediately posterior to the celiac trunk; supplies the small intestine and most of the large intestine. (Spread the mesentery of the small intestine to observe the branches of this artery as they run to supply the small intestine.)

Adrenolumbar arteries: Paired arteries diverging from the aorta slightly posterior to the superior mesenteric artery; supply the muscles of the body wall and adrenal glands.

Renal arteries: Paired arteries supplying the kidneys.

Gonadal arteries (testicular or ovarian): Paired arteries supplying the gonads.

Inferior mesenteric artery: An unpaired thin vessel arising from the ventral surface of the aorta posterior to the gonadal arteries; supplies the second half of the large intestine.

Iliolumbar arteries: Paired, rather large arteries that supply the body musculature in the iliolumbar region.

External iliac arteries: Paired arteries that continue through the body wall and pass under the inguinal ligament to the hindlimb.

6. After giving off the external iliac arteries, the aorta persists briefly and then divides into three arteries: the two **internal iliac arteries**, which supply the pelvic viscera, and the **median sacral artery**. As the median sacral artery enters the tail, it comes to be called the **caudal artery**. Note that there is no common iliac artery in the cat.

7. Trace the external iliac artery into the thigh, where it becomes the **femoral artery**. The femoral artery is most easily identified in the *femoral triangle* at the medial surface of the upper thigh. Follow the femoral artery as it courses through the thigh (along with the femoral vein and nerve) and gives off branches to the thigh muscles. As you approach the knee, the **saphenous artery** branches off the femoral artery to supply the medial portion of the leg. The femoral artery then descends deep to the knee to become the **popliteal artery** in the popliteal region. The popliteal artery in turn gives off two main branches, the **sural artery** and the **posterior tibial artery**, and continues as the **anterior tibial artery**. These branches supply the leg and foot.

8. If this activity concludes your laboratory session, follow the cleanup instructions in the accompanying box.

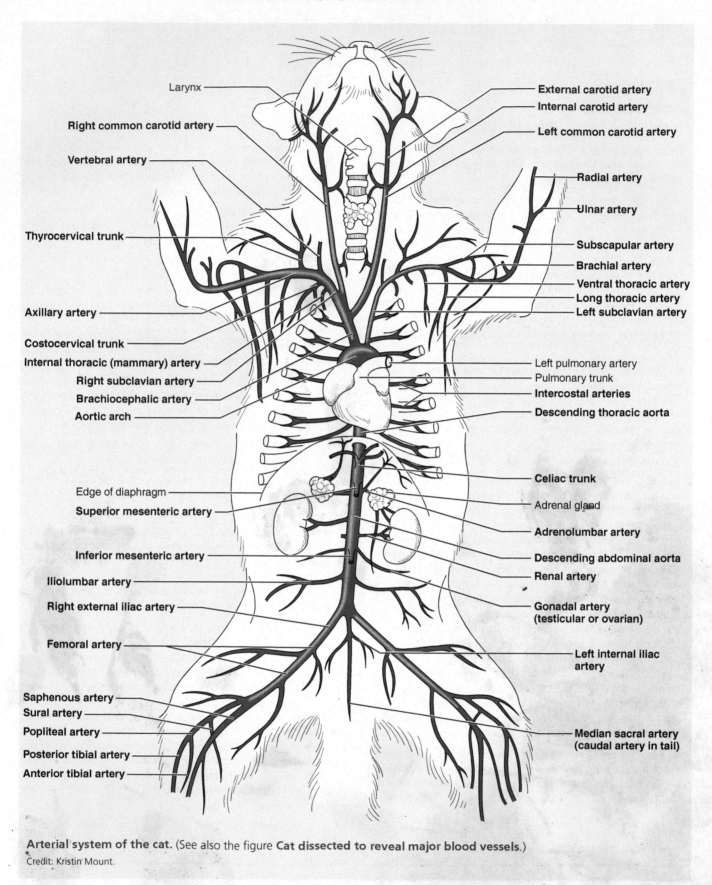

Larynx

Right common carotid artery

Vertebral artery

Thyrocervical trunk

Axillary artery

Costocervical trunk

Internal thoracic (mammary) artery

Right subclavian artery

Brachiocephalic artery

Aortic arch

Edge of diaphragm

Superior mesenteric artery

Inferior mesenteric artery

Iliolumbar artery

Right external iliac artery

Femoral artery

Saphenous artery

Sural artery

Popliteal artery

Posterior tibial artery

Anterior tibial artery

External carotid artery

Internal carotid artery

Left common carotid artery

Radial artery

Ulnar artery

Subscapular artery

Brachial artery

Ventral thoracic artery

Long thoracic artery

Left subclavian artery

Left pulmonary artery

Pulmonary trunk

Intercostal arteries

Descending thoracic aorta

Celiac trunk

Adrenal gland

Adrenolumbar artery

Descending abdominal aorta

Renal artery

Gonadal artery
(testicular or ovarian)

Left internal iliac
artery

Median sacral artery
(caudal artery in tail)

Arterial system of the cat. (See also the figure **Cat dissected to reveal major blood vessels.**)
Credit: Kristin Mount.

Dissection of the Blood Vessels of the Cat
Activity Identifying the Arteries of the Cat

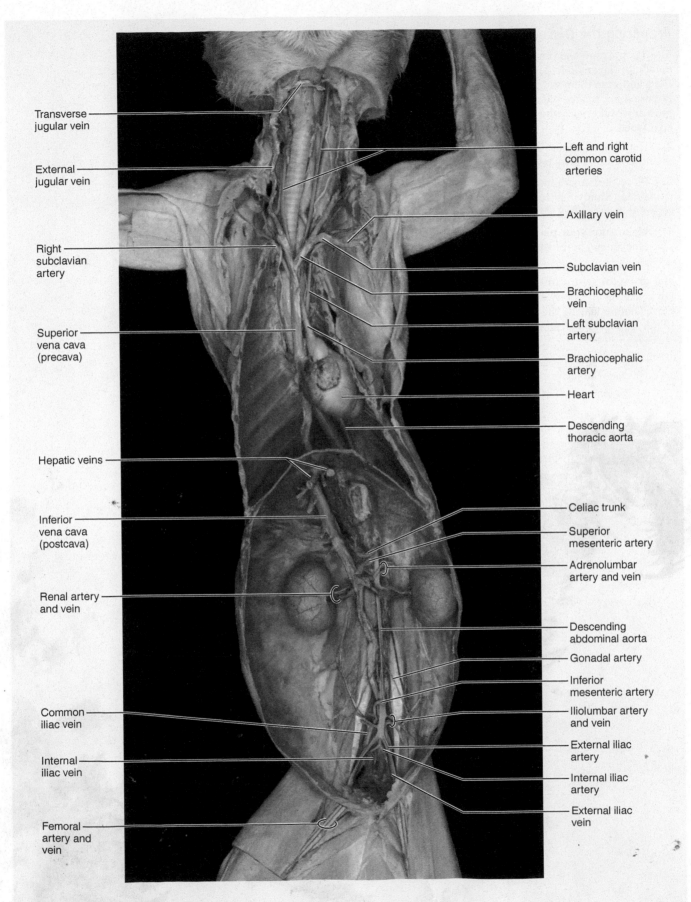

- Transverse jugular vein
- External jugular vein
- Right subclavian artery
- Superior vena cava (precava)
- Hepatic veins
- Inferior vena cava (postcava)
- Renal artery and vein
- Common iliac vein
- Internal iliac vein
- Femoral artery and vein
- Left and right common carotid arteries
- Axillary vein
- Subclavian vein
- Brachiocephalic vein
- Left subclavian artery
- Brachiocephalic artery
- Heart
- Descending thoracic aorta
- Celiac trunk
- Superior mesenteric artery
- Adrenolumbar artery and vein
- Descending abdominal aorta
- Gonadal artery
- Inferior mesenteric artery
- Iliolumbar artery and vein
- External iliac artery
- Internal iliac artery
- External iliac vein

Cat dissected to reveal major blood vessels.

Photo credits: Shawn Miller (dissection) and Mark Nielsen (photography), Pearson Education.

Preparing the Dissection Animal for Storage

1. To prevent the internal organs from drying out, dampen a layer of folded paper towels with embalming fluid, and wrap them snugly around the animal's torso. (Do not use *water-soaked* paper towels, which encourages mold growth.) Make sure the dissected areas are completely enveloped.

2. Return the animal's skin flaps to their normal position over the ventral cavity body organs.

3. Place the animal in a plastic storage bag. Add more embalming fluid if necessary, press out excess air, and securely close the bag with a rubber band or twine.

4. Make sure your name tag is securely attached, and place the animal in the designated storage container.

5. Clean all dissecting equipment with soapy water, rinse, and dry it for return to the storage area. Wash down the lab bench, and properly dispose of organic debris and your gloves before leaving the laboratory. Return safety glasses to the appropriate location.

Dissection of the Blood Vessels of the Cat
ACTIVITY Identifying the Veins of the Cat

Identifying the Veins of the Cat

Begin your dissection of the venous system of the cat. Refer to the figures **Venous system of the cat** and **Cat dissected to reveal major blood vessels**.

1. Reidentify the **superior vena cava (precava)** as it enters the right atrium. Trace it anteriorly to identify veins that enter it.

Azygos vein: Passing directly into its dorsal surface; drains the thoracic intercostal muscles.

Internal thoracic (mammary) veins: Drain the chest and abdominal walls.

Right vertebral vein: Drains the spinal cord and brain; usually enters right side of precava approximately at the level of the internal thoracic veins but may enter the brachiocephalic vein in your specimen.

Right and **left brachiocephalic veins:** Form the precava by their union.

2. Reflect the pectoral muscles, and trace the brachiocephalic vein laterally. Identify the two large veins that unite to form it—the external jugular vein and the subclavian vein. Notice that this differs from humans, whose brachiocephalic veins are formed by the union of the internal jugular and subclavian veins.

3. Follow the **external jugular vein** as it travels anteriorly along the side of the neck to the point where it is joined on its medial surface by the **internal jugular vein**. The internal jugular veins are small and may be difficult to identify in the cat. Notice the difference in cat and human jugular veins. The internal jugular is considerably larger in humans and drains into the subclavian vein. In the cat, the external jugular is larger, and the internal jugular vein drains into it. Several other vessels drain into the external jugular vein (transverse scapular vein draining the shoulder, facial veins draining the head, and others). These are not discussed here but are shown on the **Venous system of the cat** figure and may be traced if time allows. Also, identify the *common carotid artery*, since it accompanies the internal jugular vein in this region, and attempt to find the *sympathetic trunk*, which is located in the same area running lateral to the trachea.

4. Return to the shoulder region and follow the path of the **subclavian vein** as it moves laterally toward the arm. It becomes the **axillary vein** as it passes in front of the first rib and runs through the brachial plexus, giving off several branches, the first of which is the **subscapular vein**. The subscapular vein drains the proximal part of the arm and shoulder. The four other branches that receive drainage from the shoulder, pectoral, and latissimus dorsi muscles are shown in the **Venous system . . .** figure but need not be identified in this dissection.

5. Follow the axillary vein into the arm, where it becomes the **brachial vein**. You can locate this vein on the medial side of the arm accompanying the brachial artery and nerve. Trace it to the point where it receives the **radial** and **ulnar veins** (which drain the forelimb) at the inner bend of the elbow. Also locate the superficial **cephalic vein** on the dorsal side of the arm. It communicates with the brachial vein via the median cubital vein in the elbow region and then enters the transverse scapular vein in the shoulder.

6. Reidentify the **inferior vena cava (postcava)**, and trace it to its passage through the diaphragm. Notice again as you follow its course that the intercostal veins drain into a much smaller vein lying dorsal to the postcava, the **azygos vein**.

7. Attempt to identify the **hepatic veins** entering the postcava from the liver. These may be seen if some of the anterior liver tissue is scraped away where the postcava enters the liver.

8. Displace the intestines to the left side of the body cavity, and proceed posteriorly to identify the following veins in order. All of these veins empty into the postcava and drain the organs served by the same-named arteries. In the cat, variations in the connections of the veins to be located are common, and in some cases the postcaval vein may be double below the level of the renal veins. If you observe deviations, call them to the attention of your instructor.

Adrenolumbar veins: From the adrenal glands and body wall.

Renal veins: From the kidneys (it is common to find two renal veins on the right side).

Gonadal veins (testicular or ovarian veins): The left vein of this venous pair enters the left renal vein anteriorly.

Iliolumbar veins: Drain muscles of the back.

Common iliac veins: Unite to form the postcava.

The common iliac veins are formed in turn by the union of the **internal iliac** and **external iliac veins**. The more medial internal iliac veins receive branches from the pelvic organs and gluteal region, whereas the external iliac vein receives venous drainage from the lower limb. As the external iliac vein enters the thigh by running beneath the inguinal ligament, it receives the **deep femoral vein**, which drains the thigh and the external genital region. Just inferior to that point, the external iliac vein becomes the **femoral vein**, which receives blood from

Dissection of the Blood Vessels of the Cat
Activity Identifying the Veins of the Cat

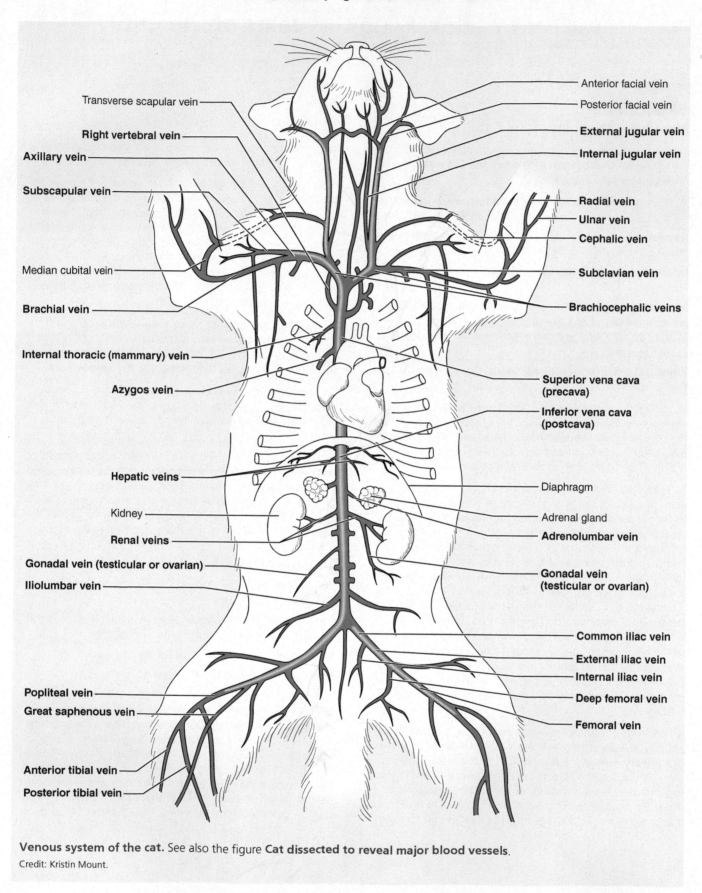

Transverse scapular vein

Right vertebral vein

Axillary vein

Subscapular vein

Median cubital vein

Brachial vein

Internal thoracic (mammary) vein

Azygos vein

Hepatic veins

Kidney

Renal veins

Gonadal vein (testicular or ovarian)

Iliolumbar vein

Popliteal vein

Great saphenous vein

Anterior tibial vein

Posterior tibial vein

Anterior facial vein

Posterior facial vein

External jugular vein

Internal jugular vein

Radial vein

Ulnar vein

Cephalic vein

Subclavian vein

Brachiocephalic veins

Superior vena cava (precava)

Inferior vena cava (postcava)

Diaphragm

Adrenal gland

Adrenolumbar vein

Gonadal vein (testicular or ovarian)

Common iliac vein

External iliac vein

Internal iliac vein

Deep femoral vein

Femoral vein

Venous system of the cat. See also the figure **Cat dissected to reveal major blood vessels**.

Credit: Kristin Mount.

Dissection of the Blood Vessels of the Cat
Activity Identifying the Veins of the Cat

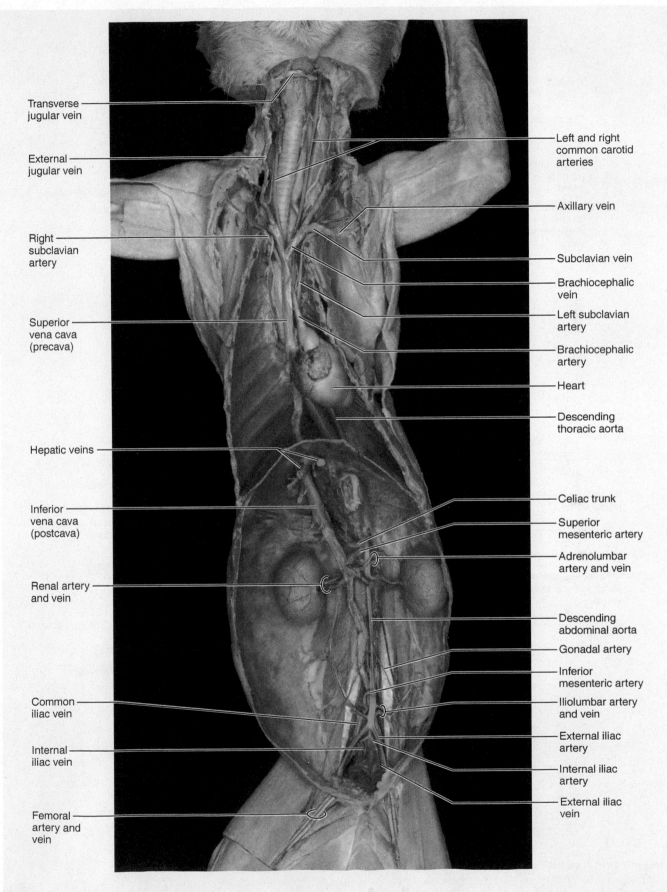

Transverse jugular vein

External jugular vein

Right subclavian artery

Superior vena cava (precava)

Hepatic veins

Inferior vena cava (postcava)

Renal artery and vein

Common iliac vein

Internal iliac vein

Femoral artery and vein

Left and right common carotid arteries

Axillary vein

Subclavian vein

Brachiocephalic vein

Left subclavian artery

Brachiocephalic artery

Heart

Descending thoracic aorta

Celiac trunk

Superior mesenteric artery

Adrenolumbar artery and vein

Descending abdominal aorta

Gonadal artery

Inferior mesenteric artery

Iliolumbar artery and vein

External iliac artery

Internal iliac artery

External iliac vein

Cat dissected to reveal major blood vessels.

Photo credits: Shawn Miller (dissection) and Mark Nielsen (photography), Pearson Education.

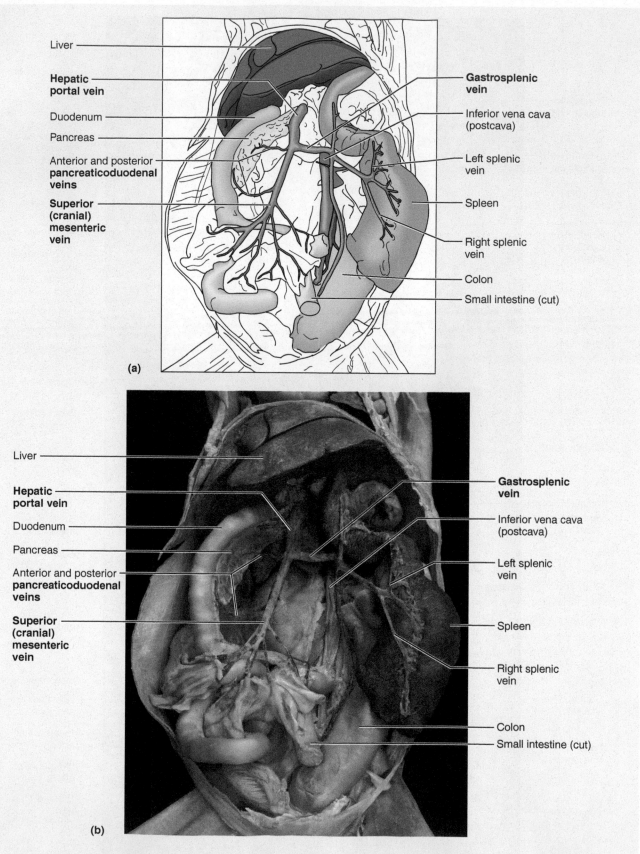

Liver

Hepatic portal vein

Duodenum

Pancreas

Anterior and posterior **pancreaticoduodenal veins**

Superior (cranial) mesenteric vein

Gastrosplenic vein

Inferior vena cava (postcava)

Left splenic vein

Spleen

Right splenic vein

Colon

Small intestine (cut)

(a)

(b)

Hepatic portal circulation of the cat. (a) Diagram. **(b)** Photograph of hepatic portal system of the cat just posterior to the liver and pancreas. Intestines have been partially removed. The mesentery of the small intestine has been partially dissected to show the veins of the portal system.

Credits: Illustration a: Imagineering STA Media Services; photo b: Shawn Miller (dissection) and Mark Nielsen (photography), Pearson Education.

the thigh, leg, and foot. Follow the femoral vein down the thigh to identify the **great saphenous vein**, a superficial vein that travels up the inner aspect of the calf and across the inferior portion of the gracilis muscle (accompanied by the great saphenous artery and nerve) to enter the femoral vein. The femoral vein is formed by the union of this vein and the popliteal vein. The **popliteal vein** is located deep in the thigh beneath the semimembranosus and semitendinosus muscles in the popliteal space accompanying the popliteal artery. Trace the popliteal vein to its point of division into the **posterior** and **anterior tibial veins**, which drain the leg.

9. Trace the hepatic portal drainage system in your cat. Refer to the figure **Hepatic portal circulation of the cat**. Locate the **hepatic portal vein** by removing the peritoneum between the first portion of the small intestine and the liver. It appears brown because of coagulated blood, and it is unlikely that it or any of the vessels of this circulation contain latex. In the cat, the hepatic portal vein is formed by the union of the gastrosplenic and superior mesenteric veins. In the human,

the hepatic portal vein is formed by the union of the splenic and superior mesenteric veins. If possible, locate the following vessels, which empty into the hepatic portal vein.

Gastrosplenic vein: Carries blood from the spleen and stomach; located dorsal to the stomach.

Superior (cranial) mesenteric vein: A large vein draining the small and large intestines and the pancreas.

Inferior (caudal) mesenteric vein (not shown): Parallels the course of the inferior mesenteric artery and empties into the superior mesenteric vein. In humans, this vessel merges with the splenic vein.

Pancreaticoduodenal veins (anterior and posterior): The anterior branch empties into the hepatic portal vein; the posterior branch empties into the superior mesenteric vein. In humans, both of these are branches of the superior mesenteric vein.

10. If this activity concludes your laboratory session, follow the cleanup instructions in the accompanying box.

Preparing the Dissection Animal for Storage

1. To prevent the internal organs from drying out, dampen a layer of folded paper towels with embalming fluid, and wrap them snugly around the animal's torso. (Do not use *water-soaked* paper towels, which encourages mold growth.) Make sure the dissected areas are completely enveloped.

2. Return the animal's skin flaps to their normal position over the ventral cavity body organs.

3. Place the animal in a plastic storage bag. Add more embalming fluid if necessary, press out excess air, and securely close the bag with a rubber band or twine.

4. Make sure your name tag is securely attached, and place the animal in the designated storage container.

5. Clean all dissecting equipment with soapy water, rinse, and dry it for return to the storage area. Wash down the lab bench, and properly dispose of organic debris and your gloves before leaving the laboratory. Return safety glasses to the appropriate location.

Dissection of the Blood Vessels of the Cat

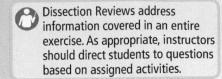

Dissection Reviews address information covered in an entire exercise. As appropriate, instructors should direct students to questions based on assigned activities.

1. What differences did you observe between the origins of the left common carotid arteries in the cat and in the human?

_____

_____

Between the origins of the internal and external iliac arteries?

_____

_____

_____

2. How do the relative sizes of the external and internal jugular veins differ in the human and the cat?

_____

_____

3. In the cat the inferior vena cava is also called the _____,

and the superior vena cava is also referred to as the _____

4. Describe the location of the following blood vessels:

ascending aorta: _____

aortic arch: _____

descending thoracic aorta: _____

descending abdominal aorta: _____

The Main Lymphatic Ducts of the Cat

Learning Outcome

▶ Compare and contrast lymphatic structures of the cat to those of a human.

Materials

- ▶ Disposable gloves
- ▶ Safety glasses
- ▶ Dissecting instruments and tray
- ▶ Animal specimen from previous dissections
- ▶ Embalming fluid
- ▶ Paper towels
- ▶ Organic debris container

Go to Mastering A&P™ > **Study Area to improve your performance in A&P Lab.**

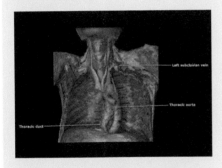

> **Lab Tools > Practice Anatomy Lab > Human Cadaver > Lymphatic System**

Instructors may assign Cat Dissection Videos, Practice Anatomy Lab Practical questions (PAL) for the dissections, and more using the Mastering A&P™ Item Library.

The Main Lymphatic Ducts of the Cat
ACTIVITY Identifying the Main Lymphatic Ducts of the Cat

Activity

Identifying the Main Lymphatic Ducts of the Cat

1. Don disposable gloves and safety glasses. Obtain your cat and a dissecting tray and instruments. Because lymphatic vessels are extremely thin walled, it is difficult to locate them in a dissection unless the animal has been triply injected (with yellow or green latex for the lymphatic system). However, the large thoracic duct can be localized and identified. Compare your observations to those of the human lymphatic system.

2. Move the thoracic organs to the side to locate the **thoracic duct**. Typically it lies just to the left of the mid-dorsal line, abutting the dorsal aspect of the descending aorta. It is usually about the size of pencil lead and red-brown with a segmented or beaded appearance caused by the valves within it. Trace it anteriorly to the site where it passes behind the left brachiocephalic vein and then bends and enters the venous system at the junction of the left subclavian and external jugular veins. If the veins are well injected, some of the blue latex may have slipped past the valves and entered the first portion of the thoracic duct.

3. While in this region, also attempt to identify the short **right lymphatic duct** draining into the right subclavian vein, and notice the collection of lymph nodes in the axillary region.

4. If the cat is triply injected, trace the thoracic duct posteriorly to identify the **cisterna chyli**, a saclike enlargement. This structure, which receives fat-rich lymph from the intestine, begins at the level of the diaphragm and can be localized posterior to the left kidney.

5. If this activity concludes your laboratory session, follow the cleanup instructions in the accompanying box.

Preparing the Dissection Animal for Storage

1. To prevent the internal organs from drying out, dampen a layer of folded paper towels with embalming fluid, and wrap them snugly around the animal's torso. (Do not use *water-soaked* paper towels, which encourages mold growth.) Make sure the dissected areas are completely enveloped.

2. Return the animal's skin flaps to their normal position over the ventral cavity body organs.

3. Place the animal in a plastic storage bag. Add more embalming fluid if necessary, press out excess air, and securely close the bag with a rubber band or twine.

4. Make sure your name tag is securely attached, and place the animal in the designated storage container.

5. Clean all dissecting equipment with soapy water, rinse, and dry it for return to the storage area. Wash down the lab bench, and properly dispose of organic debris and your gloves before leaving the laboratory. Return safety glasses to the appropriate location.

From Dissection Exercise 5, Activity 1, of *Human Anatomy & Physiology Laboratory Manual, Cat Version* Thirteenth Edition. Elaine N. Marieb and Lori Smith. Copyright © 2019 by Pearson Education, Inc. All rights reserved.

The Main Lymphatic Ducts of the Cat

1. How does the cat's lymphatic drainage pattern compare to that of humans? _____

   _____

2. What is the role of each of the following? _____

   a. thoracic duct _____

   _____

   b. right lymphatic duct _____

   _____

   c. cisterna chyli _____

   _____

Dissection of the Respiratory System of the Cat

Learning Outcome

▶ Identify the major respiratory system organs in a dissected animal.

Materials

▶ Disposable gloves
▶ Safety glasses
▶ Dissecting instruments and tray
▶ Animal specimen from previous dissections
▶ Embalming fluid
▶ Paper towels
▶ Dissecting microscope
▶ Organic debris container

n this dissection exercise, you will be examining the structure of respiratory system organs. Don disposable gloves and safety glasses, and then obtain your dissection animal and dissecting tray and instruments. Refer to a discussion of the human respiratory system as you work.

Go to Mastering A&P™ > **Study Area to improve your performance in A&P Lab.**

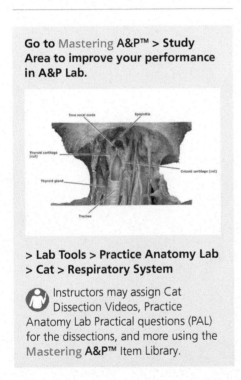

> **Lab Tools > Practice Anatomy Lab**
> **Cat > Respiratory System**

Instructors may assign Cat Dissection Videos, Practice Anatomy Lab Practical questions (PAL) for the dissections, and more using the Mastering A&P™ Item Library.

Activity

Identifying Organs of the Respiratory System

1. Examine the external nares, oral cavity, and oropharynx (see the figure **External nares, oral cavity, and pharynx of the cat**). Use a probe to demonstrate the continuity between the oropharynx and the nasopharynx above. The pharynx continues as the laryngopharynx, which lies immediately dorsal to the larynx (not shown).

2. After securing the animal to the dissecting tray dorsal surface down, expose the more distal respiratory structures by retracting the cut muscle and rib cage. Do not sever nerves and blood vessels located on either side of the trachea if these have not been studied. If you have not previously opened the thoracic cavity, make a medial longitudinal incision through the neck muscles and thoracic musculature to expose and view the thoracic organs.

3. To help you identify the structures named in steps 3 through 5, refer to the following figures: **Respiratory system of the cat**, **Larynx (opened), trachea, and thyroid gland**, and **Photograph of the respiratory system of the cat**. Examine the **trachea**, and determine by finger examination whether the cartilage rings are complete or incomplete posteriorly. Locate the **thyroid gland** inferior to the larynx on the trachea. Free the **larynx** from the attached muscle tissue for ease of examination. Identify the **thyroid** and **cricoid cartilages** and the flaplike **epiglottis**. Find the **hyoid bone**, located anterior to

the larynx. Make a longitudinal incision through the ventral wall of the larynx, and locate the vocal and vestibular folds on the inner wall (see **Larynx (opened), trachea, and thyroid gland** figure).

4. Locate the large *right* and *left common carotid arteries* and the *external jugular veins* on either side of the trachea. Also locate a conspicuous white band, the *vagus nerve*, which lies alongside the trachea, adjacent to the common carotid artery.

5. Examine the contents of the thoracic cavity (see **Photograph of the respiratory system . . .**). Follow the trachea as it bifurcates into two *main (primary) bronchi*, which plunge into the **lungs**. Note that there are two *pleural cavities* containing the lungs and that each lung is composed of many lobes. In humans there are three lobes in the right lung and two in the left. How does this compare to what is seen in the cat?

_____

_____

In the mediastinum, identify the *pericardial sac* (if it is still present) containing the heart. Examine the *pleura*, and note its exceptionally smooth texture.

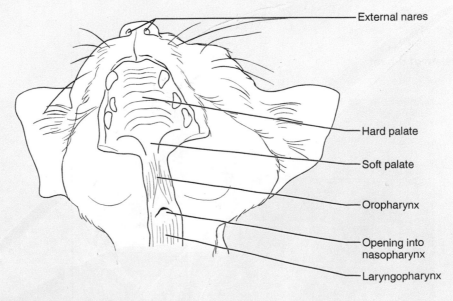

— External nares

— Hard palate

— Soft palate

— Oropharynx

— Opening into nasopharynx

— Laryngopharynx

External nares, oral cavity, and pharynx of the cat. The larynx has been dissected free and reflected toward the thorax.

Credit: Imagineering STA Media Services.

Dissection of the Respiratory System of the Cat
Activity Identifying Organs of the Respiratory System

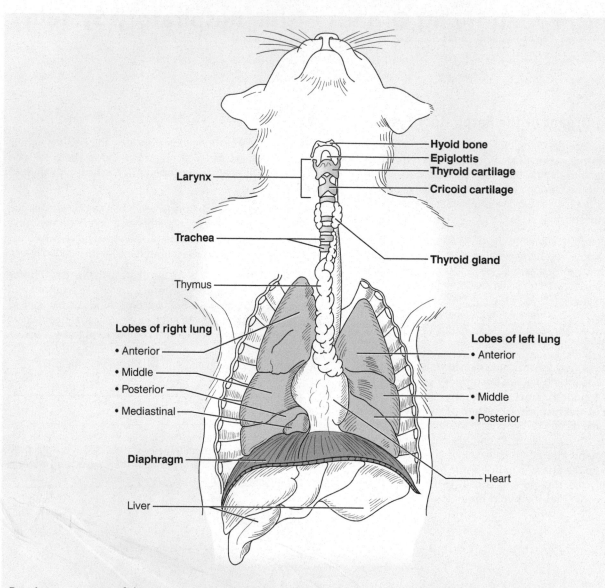

Respiratory system of the cat.

Credit: Kristin Mount.

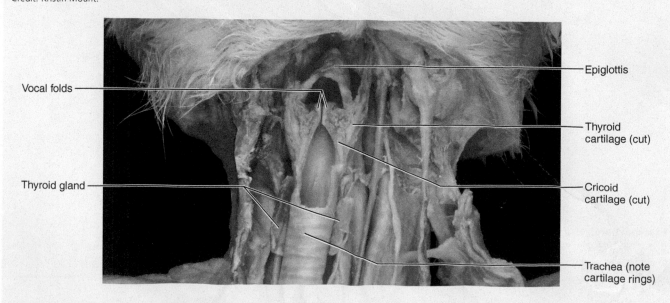

Larynx (opened), trachea, and thyroid gland.

Photo credits: Shawn Miller (dissection) and Mark Nielsen (photography), Pearson Education.

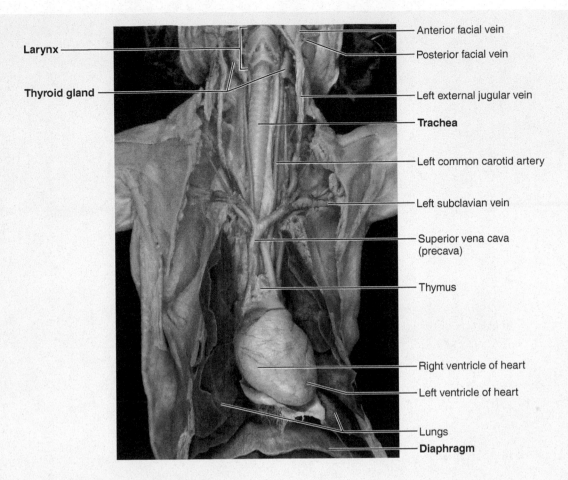

Larynx

Thyroid gland

Anterior facial vein

Posterior facial vein

Left external jugular vein

Trachea

Left common carotid artery

Left subclavian vein

Superior vena cava
(precava)

Thymus

Right ventricle of heart

Left ventricle of heart

Lungs

Diaphragm

Photograph of the respiratory system of the cat.

Photo credits: Shawn Miller (dissection) and Mark Nielsen (photography), Pearson Education.

6. Locate the **diaphragm** and the **phrenic nerve**. The phrenic nerve, clearly visible as a white "thread" running along the pericardium to the diaphragm, controls the activity of the diaphragm in breathing. Lift one lung, and find the esophagus beneath the parietal pleura. Follow it through the diaphragm to the stomach.

7. If this activity concludes your laboratory session, follow the cleanup instructions in the accompanying box.

Preparing the Dissection Animal for Storage

1. To prevent the internal organs from drying out, dampen a layer of folded paper towels with embalming fluid, and wrap them snugly around the animal's torso. (Do not use *water-soaked* paper towels, which encourages mold growth.) Make sure the dissected areas are completely enveloped.

2. Return the animal's skin flaps to their normal position over the ventral cavity body organs.

3. Place the animal in a plastic storage bag. Add more embalming fluid if necessary, press out excess air, and securely close the bag with a rubber band or twine.

4. Make sure your name tag is securely attached, and place the animal in the designated storage container.

5. Clean all dissecting equipment with soapy water, rinse, and dry it for return to the storage area. Wash down the lab bench, and properly dispose of organic debris and your gloves before leaving the laboratory. Return safety glasses to the appropriate location.

Dissection of the Respiratory System of the Cat
ACTIVITY Observing Lung Tissue Microscopically

Observing Lung Tissue Microscopically

Make a longitudinal incision in the outer tissue of one lung lobe beginning at a main bronchus. Attempt to follow part of the respiratory tree from this point down into the smaller subdivisions. Carefully observe the cut lung tissue (under a dissecting microscope, if one is available), noting the richness of the vascular supply and the irregular or spongy texture of the lung.

If this activity concludes your laboratory session, follow the cleanup instructions in the accompanying box.

Preparing the Dissection Animal for Storage

1. To prevent the internal organs from drying out, dampen a layer of folded paper towels with embalming fluid, and wrap them snugly around the animal's torso. (Do not use *water-soaked* paper towels, which encourages mold growth.) Make sure the dissected areas are completely enveloped.

2. Return the animal's skin flaps to their normal position over the ventral cavity body organs.

3. Place the animal in a plastic storage bag. Add more embalming fluid if necessary, press out excess air, and securely close the bag with a rubber band or twine.

4. Make sure your name tag is securely attached, and place the animal in the designated storage container.

5. Clean all dissecting equipment with soapy water, rinse, and dry it for return to the storage area. Wash down the lab bench, and properly dispose of organic debris and your gloves before leaving the laboratory. Return safety glasses to the appropriate location.

From Dissection Exercise 6, Activity 2, of *Human Anatomy & Physiology Laboratory Manual, Cat Version* Thirteenth Edition. Elaine N. Marieb and Lori Smith. Copyright © 2019 by Pearson Education, Inc. All rights reserved.

Dissection of the Respiratory System of the Cat

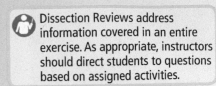

Dissection Reviews address information covered in an entire exercise. As appropriate, instructors should direct students to questions based on assigned activities.

1. Are the cartilaginous rings in the cat trachea complete or incomplete?

_____

2. Describe the appearance of the bronchial tree in the cat lung.

_____

_____

3. Describe the appearance of lung tissue under the dissection microscope.

_____

_____

Dissection of the Digestive System of the Cat

Learning Outcomes

▶ Identify on a dissected animal the organs composing the alimentary canal, and name their subdivisions if any.

▶ Name and identify the accessory organs of digestion in the dissection animal.

Materials

▶ Disposable gloves
▶ Safety glasses
▶ Dissecting instruments and tray
▶ Animal specimen from previous dissections
▶ Bone cutters
▶ Hand lens
▶ Embalming fluid
▶ Paper towels
▶ Organic debris container

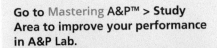

Go to Mastering A&P™ **> Study Area to improve your performance in A&P Lab.**

> Animations & Videos > Cat Dissection Videos > The Peritoneum

Instructors may assign Cat Dissection Videos, Practice Anatomy Lab Practical questions (PAL) for the dissections, and more using the Mastering A&P™ Item Library.

Don gloves and safety glasses, and obtain your dissection animal. Secure it to the dissecting tray, dorsal surface down. Obtain all necessary dissecting instruments. Refer to a discussion of the human digestive system as you work.

If the abdominal cavity has not been previously opened, make a midline incision from the rib cage to the pubic symphysis (see the figure **Incisions to be made in opening the ventral body cavity of the cat**). Then make four lateral cuts—two parallel to the rib cage and two at the inferior margin of the abdominal cavity so that the abdominal wall can be reflected back while you examine the abdominal contents. Observe the shiny membrane lining the inner surface of the abdominal wall, which is the **parietal peritoneum**.

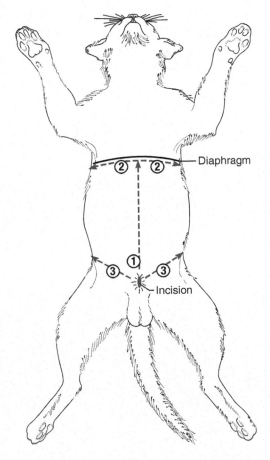

Incisions to be made in opening the ventral body cavity of the cat. Numbers indicate sequence.

Credit: Precision Graphics.

From Dissection Exercise 7, Learning Outcomes/Mastering/Materials/Introduction, of *Human Anatomy & Physiology Laboratory Manual, Cat Version* Thirteenth Edition. Elaine N. Marieb and Lori Smith. Copyright © 2019 by Pearson Education, Inc. All rights reserved.

Dissection of the Digestive System of the Cat
ACTIVITY Identifying Alimentary Canal Organs

Activity

Identifying Alimentary Canal Organs

1. Locate the abdominal alimentary canal structures. Refer to the **Digestive organs of the cat** figure.

2. Identify the large reddish brown **liver** (see the figure **Ducts of the liver and pancreas**) just beneath the diaphragm and the greater omentum, an apron of mesentery riddled with fat (not shown), that covers the abdominal contents. The greater omentum is attached to the greater curvature of the stomach; its immune cells and macrophages help to protect the abdominal cavity. Lift the greater omentum, noting its two-layered structure and attachments, and lay it to the side or remove it to make subsequent organ identifications easier. Does the liver of the cat have the same number of lobes as the human liver?

_____

_____

3. Lift the liver and examine its inferior surface to locate the **gallbladder**, a dark greenish sac embedded in the liver's ventral surface. Identify the **falciform ligament**, a delicate layer of mesentery separating the main lobes of the liver (right and left median lobes) and attaching the liver superiorly to the abdominal wall. Also identify the thickened area along the posterior edge of the falciform ligament, the *round ligament*, or *ligamentum teres*, a remnant of the umbilical vein of the fetus.

4. Displace the left lobes of the liver to expose the **stomach**. Identify the esophagus as it enters the stomach and the cardial part, fundus, body, and pyloric part of the stomach. What is the general shape of the stomach?

_____

_____

   Locate the **lesser omentum**, the serous membrane attaching the lesser curvature of the stomach to the liver, and identify the large spleen curving around the greater curvature of the stomach.
   Make an incision through the stomach wall to expose the inner surface of the stomach. When the stomach is empty, its mucosa has large folds called **rugae**. Can you see rugae? As the stomach fills, the rugae gradually disappear and are no longer visible. Identify the **pyloric sphincter** at the distal end of the stomach.

5. Lift the stomach and locate the **pancreas**, which appears as a grayish or brownish diffuse glandular mass in the mesentery. It extends from the vicinity of the spleen and greater curvature of the stomach and wraps around the duodenum. Attempt to find the **pancreatic duct** as it empties into the duodenum at a bulbous area referred to as the **hepatopancreatic ampulla** (**Ducts of the liver and pancreas** figure). Tease away the fine connective tissue, locate the **bile duct** close to the pancreatic duct, and trace its path superiorly to the point where it diverges into the **cystic duct** (gallbladder duct) and the **common hepatic duct** (duct from the liver). Notice that the duodenum assumes a looped position.

6. Lift the **small intestine** to investigate the manner in which it is attached to the posterior body wall by the **mesentery**.

Observe the mesentery closely. What types of structures do you see in this double peritoneal fold?

_____

_____

Other than providing support for the intestine, what functions does the mesentery have?

_____

_____

_____

Trace the path of the small intestine from its proximal (duodenal) end to its distal (ileal) end. Can you see any obvious differences in the external anatomy of the small intestine from one end to the other?

_____

_____

With a scalpel, slice open the distal portion of the ileum and flush out the inner surface with water. Feel the inner surface with your fingertip. How does it feel?

_____

_____

Use a hand lens to see whether you can see any **villi** and to locate the areas of lymphatic tissue called **Peyer's patches**, which appear as scattered white patches on the inner intestinal surface.
   Return to the duodenal end of the small intestine. Make an incision into the duodenum. As before, flush the surface with water, and feel the inner surface. Does it feel any different from the ileal mucosa?

_____ If so, describe the difference. _____

_____

Use the hand lens to observe the villi. What differences do you see in the villi in the two areas of the small intestine?

_____

_____

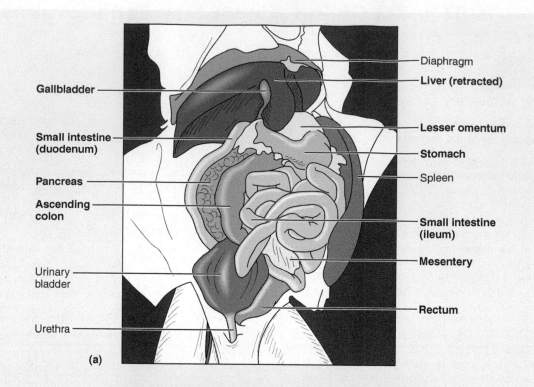

(a)

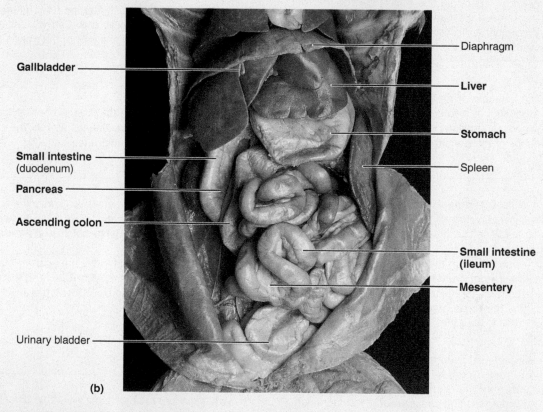

(b)

Digestive organs of the cat. (a) Diagram. **(b)** Photograph. The greater omentum has been cut from its attachment to the stomach.

Credits: Illustration a: Kristin Mount; photo b: Elena Dorfman, Pearson Education.

7. Make an incision into the junction between the ileum and cecum to locate the ileocecal valve (see the **Ileocecal valve** figure). Observe the **cecum**, the initial expanded part of the large intestine. You may have to remove lymph nodes from this area to observe it clearly. Does the cat have an appendix?

Dissection of the Digestive System of the Cat
Activity Identifying Alimentary Canal Organs

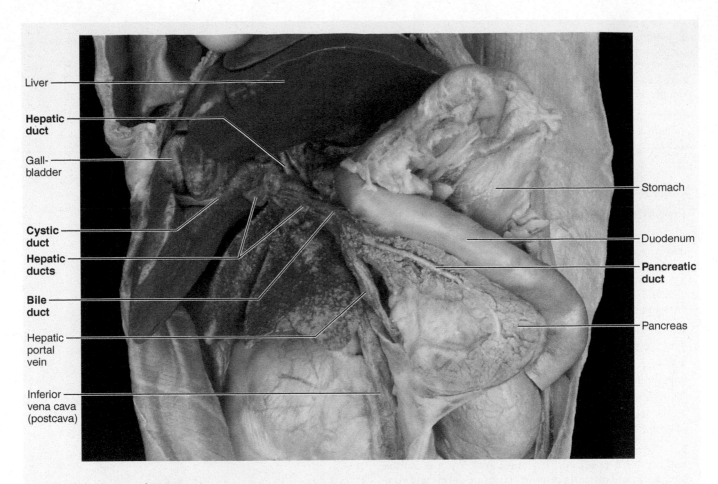

Liver

Hepatic duct

Gall-bladder

Cystic duct

Hepatic ducts

Bile duct

Hepatic portal vein

Inferior vena cava (postcava)

Stomach

Duodenum

Pancreatic duct

Pancreas

Ducts of the liver and pancreas.

Photo credits: Shawn Miller (dissection) and Mark Nielsen (photography), Pearson Education.

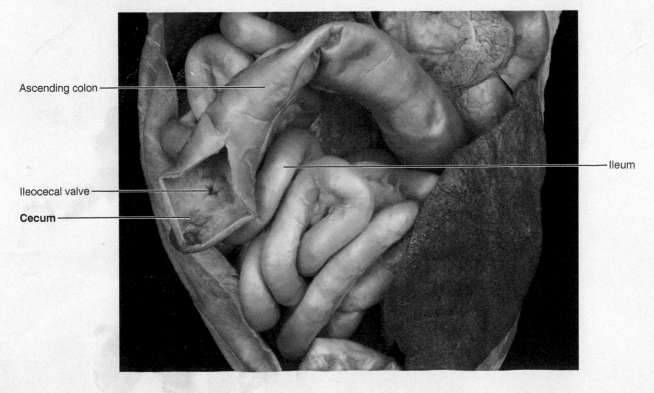

Ascending colon

Ileocecal valve

Cecum

Ileum

Ileocecal valve.

Photo credits: Shawn Miller (dissection) and Mark Nielsen (photography), Pearson Education.

8. Identify the short ascending, transverse, and descending portions of the **colon** and the **mesocolon**, a membrane that attaches the colon to the posterior body wall. Trace the descending colon to the **rectum**, which penetrates the body wall, and identify the **anus** on the exterior surface of the specimen.

Identify the two portions of the peritoneum, the parietal peritoneum lining the abdominal wall (identified previously) and the visceral peritoneum, which is the outermost layer of the wall of the abdominal organs.

9. If this activity concludes your laboratory session, follow the cleanup instructions in the accompanying box.

Preparing the Dissection Animal for Storage

1. To prevent the internal organs from drying out, dampen a layer of folded paper towels with embalming fluid, and wrap them snugly around the animal's torso. (Do not use *water-soaked* paper towels, which encourages mold growth.) Make sure the dissected areas are completely enveloped.

2. Return the animal's skin flaps to their normal position over the ventral cavity body organs.

3. Place the animal in a plastic storage bag. Add more embalming fluid if necessary, press out excess air, and securely close the bag with a rubber band or twine.

4. Make sure your name tag is securely attached, and place the animal in the designated storage container.

5. Clean all dissecting equipment with soapy water, rinse, and dry it for return to the storage area. Wash down the lab bench, and properly dispose of organic debris and your gloves before leaving the laboratory. Return safety glasses to the appropriate location.

Dissection of the Digestive System of the Cat
ACTIVITY Exposing and Viewing the Salivary Glands and Oral Cavity Structures

Exposing and Viewing the Salivary Glands and Oral Cavity Structures

1. To expose and identify the **salivary glands**, remove the skin from one side of the head and clear the connective tissue away from the angle of the jaw, below the ear, and superior to the masseter muscle. Many lymph nodes are in this area, and you should remove them if they obscure the salivary glands, which are lighter tan and lobular in texture. The cat possesses five pairs of salivary glands, but only those glands described in humans are easily localized and identified (see the **Salivary glands of the cat** figure). Locate the **parotid gland** on the cheek just inferior to the ear. Follow its duct over the surface of the masseter muscle to the angle of the mouth.

The **submandibular gland** is posterior to the parotid, near the angle of the jaw, and the **sublingual gland** (not shown in the **figure**) is just anterior to the submandibular gland within the lower jaw. The ducts of the submandibular and sublingual glands run deep and parallel to each other and empty on the side of the frenulum of the tongue. These need not be identified on the cat.

2. To expose and identify the structures of the oral cavity, cut through the mandibular angle with bone cutters to free the lower jaw from the maxilla.

Identify the **hard** and **soft palates**, and use a probe to trace the bony hard palate to its posterior limits. Note the transverse ridges, or *rugae*, on the hard palate, which play a role in holding food in place while chewing.

Do these appear in humans? _____

Does the cat have a uvula? _____

Identify the **oropharynx** at the rear of the oral cavity and the palatine tonsils on the posterior walls at the junction between the oral cavity and oropharynx. Identify the **tongue**, and rub your finger across its surface to feel the papillae. Some of the papillae, especially at the anterior end of the tongue, should feel sharp and bristly. These are the filiform papillae. What do you think their function is?

_____

Locate the **lingual frenulum** attaching the tongue to the floor of the mouth. Trace the tongue posteriorly until you locate the **epiglottis**, the flap of tissue that covers the entrance to the respiratory passageway when swallowing occurs. Identify the **esophageal opening** posterior to the epiglottis.

Observe the **teeth** of the cat. The dental formula for the adult cat is as follows:

$$\frac{3,1,3,1}{3,1,2,1} \times 2 = 30$$

3. If this activity concludes your laboratory session, follow the cleanup instructions in the accompanying box.

Preparing the Dissection Animal for Storage

1. To prevent the internal organs from drying out, dampen a layer of folded paper towels with embalming fluid, and wrap them snugly around the animal's torso. (Do not use *water-soaked* paper towels, which encourages mold growth.) Make sure the dissected areas are completely enveloped.

2. Return the animal's skin flaps to their normal position over the ventral cavity body organs.

3. Place the animal in a plastic storage bag. Add more embalming fluid if necessary, press out excess air, and securely close the bag with a rubber band or twine.

4. Make sure your name tag is securely attached, and place the animal in the designated storage container.

5. Clean all dissecting equipment with soapy water, rinse, and dry it for return to the storage area. Wash down the lab bench, and properly dispose of organic debris and your gloves before leaving the laboratory. Return safety glasses to the appropriate location.

From Dissection Exercise 7, Activity 2, of *Human Anatomy & Physiology Laboratory Manual, Cat Version* Thirteenth Edition. Elaine N. Marieb and Lori Smith. Copyright © 2019 by Pearson Education, Inc. All rights reserved.

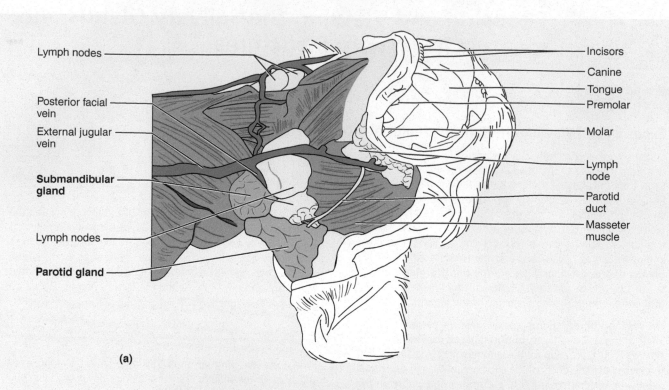

Lymph nodes

Posterior facial
vein

External jugular
vein

**Submandibular
gland**

Lymph nodes

Parotid gland

Incisors

Canine

Tongue

Premolar

Molar

Lymph
node

Parotid
duct

Masseter
muscle

(a)

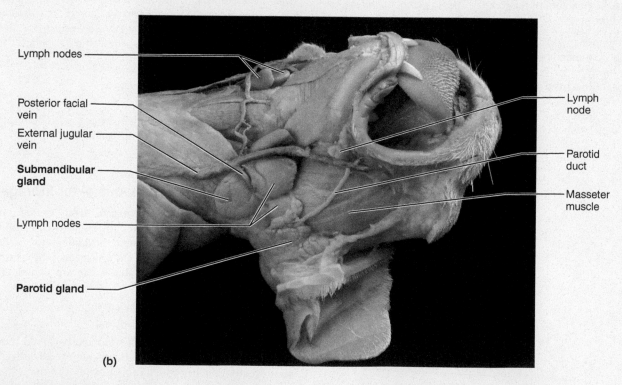

Lymph nodes

Posterior facial
vein

External jugular
vein

**Submandibular
gland**

Lymph nodes

Parotid gland

Lymph
node

Parotid
duct

Masseter
muscle

(b)

Salivary glands of the cat. (a) Diagram. **(b)** Photograph.

Credits: Illustration a: Imagineering STA Media Services; photo b: Shawn Miller (dissection) and Mark Nielsen
(photography), Pearson Education.

Dissection of the Digestive System of the Cat

> Dissection Reviews address information covered in an entire exercise. As appropriate, instructors should direct students to questions based on assigned activities.

1. Compare the appearance of tongue papillae in cats and humans. _____

   _____

2. Compare the number of lobes of the liver in cats and humans. _____

   _____

3. Does the cat have a uvula? _____ An appendix? _____

4. Give an explanation for the different adult dental formulas in cats and humans.

   _____

   _____

5. How do the villi differ in the duodenum and the ileum? Explain.

   _____

   _____

From Dissection Exercise 7, Dissection Review, of *Human Anatomy & Physiology Laboratory Manual, Cat Version* Thirteenth Edition. Elaine N. Marieb and Lori Smith. Copyright © 2019 by Pearson Education, Inc. All rights reserved.

Dissection of the Urinary System of the Cat

Learning Outcome

▶ Identify the urinary system organs on a dissection specimen.

Materials

▶ Disposable gloves
▶ Safety glasses
▶ Dissecting instruments and tray
▶ Animal specimen from previous dissections
▶ Hand magnifying lens
▶ Embalming fluid
▶ Paper towel
▶ Organic debris container

Go to Mastering A&P™ **> Study Area to improve your performance in A&P Lab.**

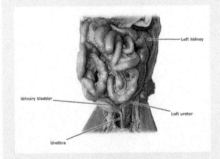

> Lab Tools > Practice Anatomy Lab > Cat > Urinary System

Instructors may assign Cat Dissection Videos, Practice Anatomy Lab Practical questions (PAL) for the dissections, and more using the Mastering A&P™ Item Library.

The structures of the reproductive and urinary systems are often considered together as the *urogenital system*, since they have common embryological origins. However, in dissections of a specimen it is useful to study the systems separately. Here we will identify the structures of the urinary tract, with only a few references to neighboring reproductive structures. Refer to a discussion of the human urinary system as you work.

Dissection of the Urinary System of the Cat
ACTIVITY Identifying Organs of the Urinary System

Activity

Identifying Organs of the Urinary System

1. Don gloves and safety glasses. Obtain your dissection specimen, and place it ventral side up on the dissecting tray. Reflect the abdominal viscera (in particular, the small intestine) to locate the kidneys high on the dorsal body wall. Refer to the figures **Urinary system of the female cat** and **Urinary system of the male cat**. Note that the **kidneys** in the cat, as well as in the human, are retroperitoneal (behind the peritoneum). Carefully remove the peritoneum, and clear away the bed of fat that surrounds the kidneys. Then locate the adrenal glands that lie superiorly and medial to the kidneys.

2. Identify the **renal artery** (red latex injected), the **renal vein** (blue latex injected), and the ureter at the hilum region of the kidney. You may find two renal veins leaving one kidney in the cat, but not in humans.

3. To observe the gross internal anatomy of the kidney, slit the connective tissue *fibrous capsule* encasing a kidney, and peel it back. Make a midfrontal cut through the kidney, and examine one cut surface with a hand lens to identify the granular *cortex* and the central darker *medulla*, which will appear striated. Notice that the cat's renal medulla consists of just one pyramid as compared to the multipyramidal human kidney.

4. Trace the tubelike **ureters** to the **urinary bladder**, a smooth muscular sac located superior to the small intestine. If your cat is a female, be careful not to confuse the ureters with the uterine tubes, which lie superior to the bladder in the same general region (see **Urinary system of the female cat** figure). Observe the sites where the ureters enter the bladder. How would you describe the entrance point anatomically?

_____

_____

5. Cut through the bladder wall, and examine the region where the **urethra** exits to see if you can discern any evidence of the *internal urethral sphincter*.

6. If your cat is a male, identify the prostate (part of the male reproductive system), which encircles the urethra distal to the neck of the bladder (see **Urinary system of the male cat** figure). Notice that the urinary bladder is somewhat fixed in position by ligaments.

7. Using a probe, trace the urethra as it exits from the bladder. In the male, it enters the penis. In the female cat, it terminates in the **urogenital sinus**, a common chamber into which both the vagina and the urethra empty. In the human female, the vagina and the urethra have separate external openings. At this time, do not perform dissection to expose the urethra along its entire length, because you might damage the reproductive structures, which you may study in a separate exercise.

8. To complete this exercise, observe a cat of the opposite sex. If this activity concludes your laboratory session, follow the cleanup instructions in the accompanying box.

Preparing the Dissection Animal for Storage

1. To prevent the internal organs from drying out, dampen a layer of folded paper towels with embalming fluid, and wrap them snugly around the animal's torso. (Do not use *water-soaked* paper towels, which encourages mold growth.) Make sure the dissected areas are completely enveloped.

2. Return the animal's skin flaps to their normal position over the ventral cavity body organs.

3. Place the animal in a plastic storage bag. Add more embalming fluid if necessary, press out excess air, and securely close the bag with a rubber band or twine.

4. Make sure your name tag is securely attached, and place the animal in the designated storage container.

5. Clean all dissecting equipment with soapy water, rinse, and dry it for return to the storage area. Wash down the lab bench, and properly dispose of organic debris and your gloves before leaving the laboratory. Return safety glasses to the appropriate location.

From Dissection Exercise 8, Activity 1, of *Human Anatomy & Physiology Laboratory Manual, Cat Version* Thirteenth Edition. Elaine N. Marieb and Lori Smith. Copyright © 2019 by Pearson Education, Inc. All rights reserved.

Dissection of the Urinary System of the Cat
Activity Identifying Organs of the Urinary System

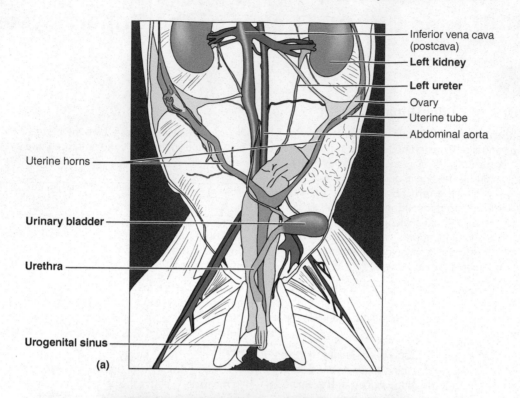

Inferior vena cava (postcava)

Left kidney

Left ureter

Ovary

Uterine tube

Abdominal aorta

Uterine horns

Urinary bladder

Urethra

Urogenital sinus

(a)

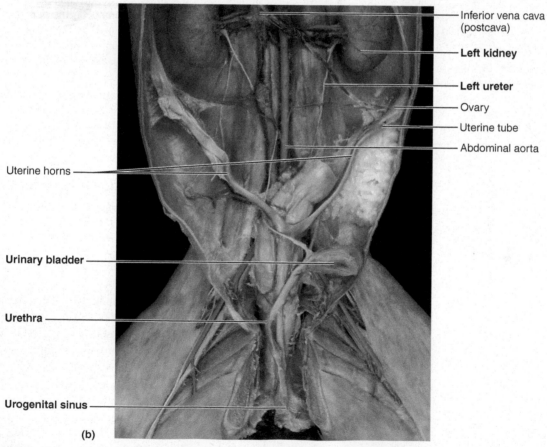

Inferior vena cava (postcava)

Left kidney

Left ureter

Ovary

Uterine tube

Abdominal aorta

Uterine horns

Urinary bladder

Urethra

Urogenital sinus

(b)

Urinary system of the female cat. (Reproductive structures are also indicated.) **(a)** Diagram. **(b)** Photograph of female urogenital system.

Credits: Illustration a: Imagineering STA Media Services; photo b: Shawn Miller (dissection) and Mark Nielsen (photography), Pearson Education.

Dissection of the Urinary System of the Cat
Activity Identifying Organs of the Urinary System

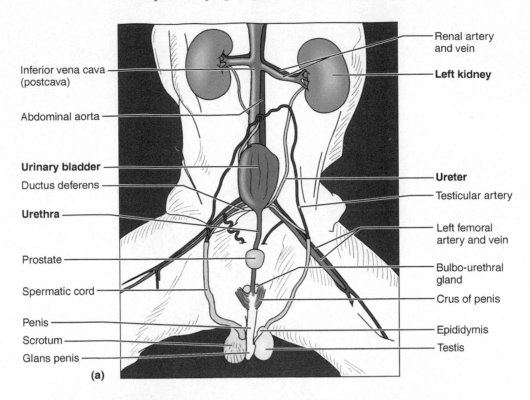

Inferior vena cava (postcava)

Abdominal aorta

Urinary bladder

Ductus deferens

Urethra

Prostate

Spermatic cord

Penis

Scrotum

Glans penis

Renal artery and vein

Left kidney

Ureter

Testicular artery

Left femoral artery and vein

Bulbo-urethral gland

Crus of penis

Epididymis

Testis

(a)

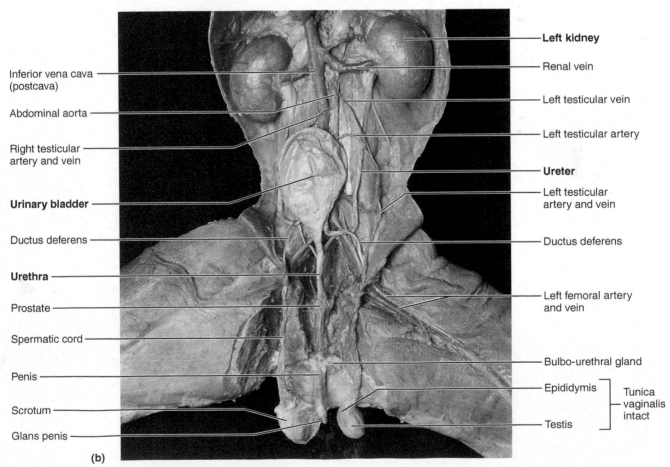

Inferior vena cava (postcava)

Abdominal aorta

Right testicular artery and vein

Urinary bladder

Ductus deferens

Urethra

Prostate

Spermatic cord

Penis

Scrotum

Glans penis

Left kidney

Renal vein

Left testicular vein

Left testicular artery

Ureter

Left testicular artery and vein

Ductus deferens

Left femoral artery and vein

Bulbo-urethral gland

Epididymis

Testis

Tunica vaginalis intact

(b)

Urinary system of the male cat. (Reproductive structures are also indicated.) **(a)** Diagram. **(b)** Photograph of male urogenital system.

Credits: Illustration a: Kristin Mount; photo b: Elena Dorfman, Pearson Education.

Dissection of the Urinary System of the Cat

1. a. How does the position of the kidneys in the cat differ from their position in humans?

    _____

    _____

    b. In what way is the position similar?

    _____

2. Distinguish between the functions of a ureter and those of the urethra.

    _____

    _____

3. How does the site of urethral emptying in the female cat differ from its termination point in the human female?

    _____

    _____

4. What is a urogenital sinus?

    _____

5. What gland encircles the neck of the bladder in the male? _____ Is this part of the urinary system?

    _____ What is its function? _____

    _____

6. Compare the location of the adrenal glands in the cat to the location in humans.

    _____

    _____

Dissection of the Reproductive System of the Cat

Learning Outcomes

▶ Identify the major reproductive structures of a male and a female dissection animal.

▶ Recognize and discuss pertinent differences between the reproductive structures of humans and the dissection animal.

Materials

▶ Disposable gloves
▶ Safety glasses
▶ Dissecting instruments and tray
▶ Animal specimen from previous dissections
▶ Bone cutters
▶ Small metric rulers (for female cats)
▶ Embalming fluid
▶ Paper towels
▶ Organic debris container

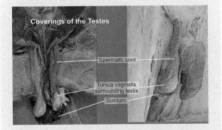
Don gloves and safety glasses. Obtain your cat, a dissecting tray, and the necessary dissecting instruments. After you have completed the study of the reproductive structures of your specimen, observe a cat of the opposite sex. The following instructions assume that the abdominal cavity has been opened. Refer to a discussion of the human reproductive system as you work.

Dissection of the Reproductive System of the Cat
ACTIVITY Identifying Organs of the Male Reproductive System

Identifying Organs of the Male Reproductive System

Identify the male reproductive structures. Refer to the **Reproductive system of the male cat** figure.

1. Identify the **penis**, and notice the prepuce covering the glans. Carefully cut through the skin overlying the penis to expose the cavernous tissue beneath, then cross section the penis to see the relative positioning of the three cavernous bodies.

2. Identify the **scrotum**, and then carefully make a shallow incision through the scrotum to expose the **testes**. Notice the abundant connective tissue stretching between the inner wall of the scrotum and testis surface, and note that the scrotum is divided internally.

3. Lateral to the medial aspect of the scrotal sac, locate the **spermatic cord**, which contains the testicular artery, vein, and nerve, as well as the ductus deferens, and follow it up through the inguinal canal into the abdominal cavity. It is not necessary to cut through the pubis; a slight tug on the spermatic cord in the scrotal sac region will reveal its position in the abdominal cavity. Carefully loosen the spermatic cord from the connective tissue investing it, and follow its course as it travels superiorly in the pelvic cavity. Then follow the **ductus deferens** as it loops over the ureter and then courses posterior to the bladder and enters the prostate. Using bone cutters, carefully cut through the pubic symphysis to follow the urethra.

4. Notice that the **prostate**, an enlarged whitish glandular mass abutting the urethra, is comparatively smaller in the cat than in the human, and it is more distal to the bladder. In the human, the prostate is immediately adjacent to the base of the bladder. Carefully slit open the prostate to follow the ductus deferens to the urethra. The male cat urethra, like that of the human, serves as both a urinary and a sperm duct. In the human, the ductus deferens is joined by the duct of the seminal gland to form the ejaculatory duct, which enters the prostate. Seminal glands are not present in the cat.

5. Trace the **urethra** to the proximal ends of the cavernous tissues of the penis, each of which is anchored to the ischium by a band of connective tissue called the **crus** of the penis. The crus is covered ventrally by the ischiocavernosus muscle, and the **bulbo-urethral gland** lies beneath it (see **Reproductive system of the male cat** figure).

6. Once again, turn your attention to the testis. Cut it from its attachment to the spermatic cord, and carefully slit open the **tunica vaginalis** capsule enclosing it. Identify the **epididymis** running along one side of the testis. Make a longitudinal cut through the testis and epididymis. Can you see the tubular nature of the epididymis and the rete testis portion of the testis with the naked eye?

7. If this activity concludes your laboratory session, follow the cleanup instructions in the accompanying box.

Preparing the Dissection Animal for Storage

1. To prevent the internal organs from drying out, dampen a layer of folded paper towels with embalming fluid, and wrap them snugly around the animal's torso. (Do not use *water-soaked* paper towels, which encourages mold growth.) Make sure the dissected areas are completely enveloped.

2. Return the animal's skin flaps to their normal position over the ventral cavity body organs.

3. Place the animal in a plastic storage bag. Add more embalming fluid if necessary, press out excess air, and securely close the bag with a rubber band or twine.

4. Make sure your name tag is securely attached, and place the animal in the designated storage container.

5. Clean all dissecting equipment with soapy water, rinse, and dry it for return to the storage area. Wash down the lab bench, and properly dispose of organic debris and your gloves before leaving the laboratory. Return safety glasses to the appropriate location.

From Dissection Exercise 9, Activity 1, of *Human Anatomy & Physiology Laboratory Manual, Cat Version* Thirteenth Edition. Elaine N. Marieb and Lori Smith. Copyright © 2019 by Pearson Education, Inc. All rights reserved.

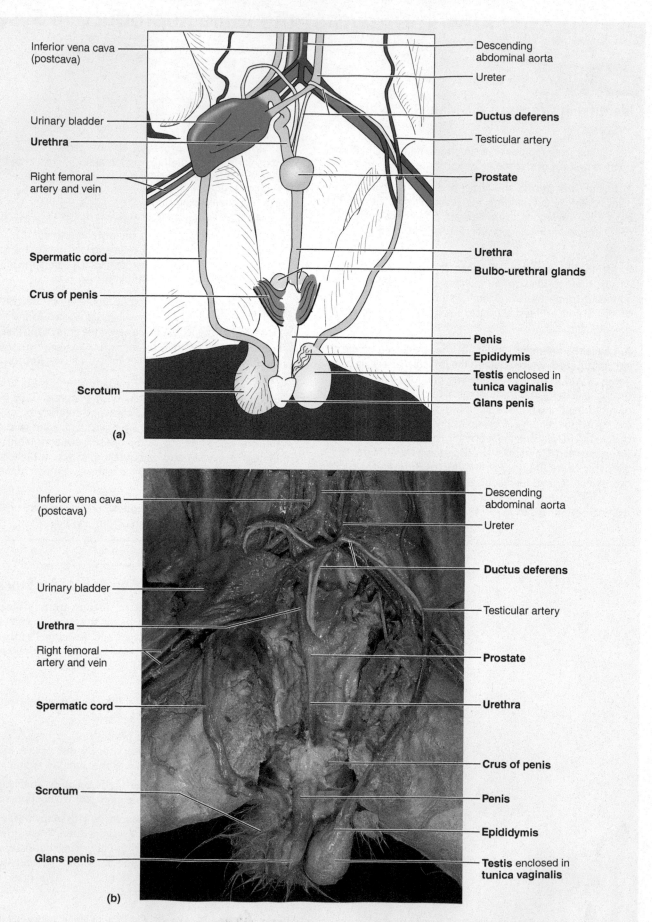

Reproductive system of the male cat. (a) Diagram. **(b)** Photograph.

Credits: Illustration a: Kristin Mount; photo b: Paul Waring, Pearson Education.

Dissection of the Reproductive System of the Cat
ACTIVITY Identifying Organs of the Female Reproductive System

Activity

Identifying Organs of the Female Reproductive System

Identify the female reproductive structures. Refer to the **Reproductive system of the female cat** figure.

1. Unlike the pear-shaped simplex, or one-part, uterus of the human, the uterus of the cat is Y-shaped (bipartite, or bicornuate) and consists of a **uterine body** from which two **uterine horns** diverge. Such an enlarged uterus enables the animal to produce litters. Examine the abdominal cavity, and identify the bladder and the body of the uterus lying just dorsal to it.

2. Follow one of the uterine horns as it travels superiorly in the body cavity. Identify the thin mesentery (the *broad ligament*) that helps anchor it and the other reproductive structures to the body wall. Approximately halfway up the length of the uterine horn, it should be possible to identify the more important *round ligament*, a cord of connective tissue extending laterally and posteriorly from the uterine horn to the region of the body wall that would correspond to the inguinal region of the male.

3. Examine the **uterine tube** and **ovary** at the distal end of the uterine horn just caudal to the kidney. Observe how the funnel-shaped end of the uterine tube curves around the ovary. As in the human, the distal end of the tube is fimbriated, or fringed, and the tube is lined with ciliated epithelium. The uterine tubes of the cat are tiny and much shorter than in the human. Identify the **ovarian ligament**, a short, thick cord that extends from the uterus to the ovary and anchors the ovary to the body wall. Also observe the *ovarian artery* and *vein* passing through the mesentery to the ovary and uterine structures.

4. Return to the body of the uterus, and follow it caudally to the pelvis. Use bone cutters to cut through the pubic symphysis, cutting carefully so you do not damage the urethra deep to it. Expose the pelvic region by pressing the thighs dorsally. Follow the uterine body caudally to where it narrows to its sphincterlike cervix, which protrudes into the vagina. Note the point where the urethra draining the bladder and the **vagina** enter a common chamber, the **urogenital sinus.** How does this anatomical arrangement compare to that seen in the human female?

_____

_____

5. On the cat's exterior, observe the **vulva**, which is similar to the human vulva. Identify the slim **labia majora** surrounding the urogenital opening.

6. To determine the length of the vagina, which is difficult to ascertain by external inspection, slit through the vaginal wall just superior to the urogenital sinus, and cut toward the body of the uterus with scissors. Reflect the cut edges, and identify the muscular cervix of the uterus. Measure the distance between the urogenital sinus and the cervix. Approximately how long is the vagina of the cat?

_____

7. To complete this exercise, observe a cat of the opposite sex.

8. If this activity concludes your laboratory session, follow the cleanup instructions in the accompanying box.

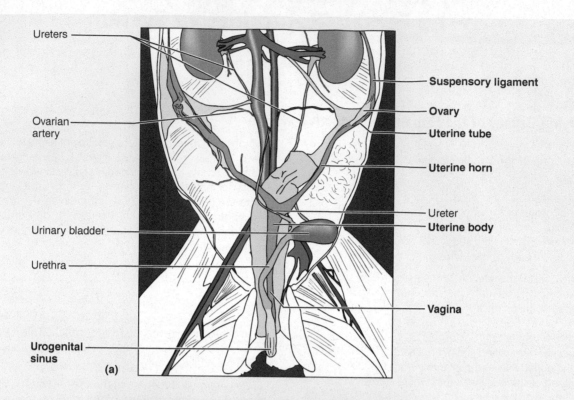

Ureters

Ovarian artery

Urinary bladder

Urethra

Urogenital sinus

(a)

Suspensory ligament

Ovary

Uterine tube

Uterine horn

Ureter

Uterine body

Vagina

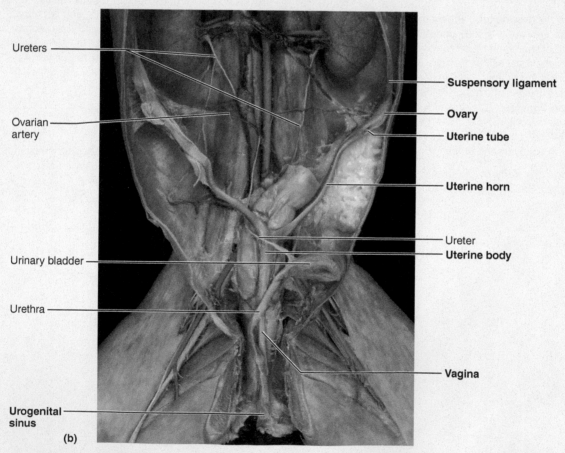

Ureters

Ovarian artery

Urinary bladder

Urethra

Urogenital sinus

(b)

Suspensory ligament

Ovary

Uterine tube

Uterine horn

Ureter

Uterine body

Vagina

Reproductive system of the female cat. (a) Diagram. **(b)** Photograph.

Credits: Illustration a: Imagineering STA Media Services; photo b: Shawn Miller (dissection) and Mark Nielsen (photography), Pearson Education.

Preparing the Dissection Animal for Storage

1. To prevent the internal organs from drying out, dampen a layer of folded paper towels with embalming fluid, and wrap them snugly around the animal's torso. (Do not use *water-soaked* paper towels, which encourages mold growth.) Make sure the dissected areas are completely enveloped.

2. Return the animal's skin flaps to their normal position over the ventral cavity body organs.

3. Place the animal in a plastic storage bag. Add more embalming fluid if necessary, press out excess air, and securely close the bag with a rubber band or twine.

4. Make sure your name tag is securely attached, and place the animal in the designated storage container.

5. Clean all dissecting equipment with soapy water, rinse, and dry it for return to the storage area. Wash down the lab bench, and properly dispose of organic debris and your gloves before leaving the laboratory. Return safety glasses to the appropriate location.

Dissection of the Reproductive System of the Cat

1. The female cat has a _____ uterus; that of the human female is _____.

    Explain the difference in structure of these two uterine types. _____

    _____

    _____

2. What reproductive advantage is conferred by the feline uterine type?

    _____

    _____

3. Cite differences noted between the cat and the human relative to the following structures:

    uterine tubes _____

    _____

    site of entry of ductus deferens into the urethra _____

    _____

    location of the prostate _____

    _____

    seminal glands _____

    urethral and vaginal openings in the female _____

    _____

    _____

From Dissection Exercise 9, Dissection Review, of *Human Anatomy & Physiology Laboratory Manual, Cat Version* Thirteenth Edition. Elaine N. Marieb and Lori Smith. Copyright © 2019 by Pearson Education, Inc. All rights reserved.

Index